C A L M

By

Stephen A. Schacher, M.D.

This book is written for informational purposes only. It should not be considered a substitute for the advice of a qualified medical professional as the needs of specific individuals vary. Every effort has been made to authenticate the accuracy of the information contained herein, as of the date published. The author and the publisher expressly disclaim any responsibility for any adverse effects arising from the use or application of the information contained herein.

Second edition published 2010 by Perisseia Publishing, perisseiapublishing@gmail.com
1290 Allgood Road, Athens, GA 30606.

Designed by Roberta Kern Schacher
Illustrations by Nicole Manning
Graphic Design by Angel Breitenbach

ISBN 978-0-96625291-0

ACKNOWLEDGEMENTS

I would like to thank Nicole Manning for her lovely drawings and diagrams, my patients for their wonderful suggestions, and my wife Roberta for her calm spirit and love of learning.

FOREWORD

Calm is the opposite of stress.

For many years I gave stress talks to my internal medicine patients in Seattle, because I was certain that their reactions to stress were making every aspect of their health worse. To learn how to deal more effectively with stress, we would meet on Saturday mornings, discuss the stress reaction itself, hear people describe the bad choices they had made under stress, and try to see in retrospect what each of us could have done in various stressful situations to produce a better outcome.

In the relaxed mood of an informal Saturday morning meeting, looking out our office windows onto beautiful Lake Union, it was easy to be more creative and inventive than any of us had been during the week. I tried to keep track of the suggestions that people made, categorize them into strategies for dealing with stress, and then practice what we had learned to be more effective in the coming weeks.

A lot of the suggestions worked. At first I thought it was just a matter of being relaxed, but soon all of us began to realize that when we were relaxed, we were also more observant, creative, ethical, and intelligent. We noted that humor was more effective when relaxed and more sarcastic and spiteful when we were stressed. We found that we learned new information more easily when relaxed and that we fought off new ideas when we were stressed.

And so we tried to find strategies that would take us from the stressed state to the relaxed state, so that we could take advantage of these talents that arose magically if we could just keep our minds and bodies relaxed.

When I started to write this book, I called these strategies, "the opposites of stress", and in Part III, I discuss some of them. But soon I became aware that there are as many strategies for overcoming stress as there are people willing to be creative in difficult situations. I searched instead for something that linked them all.

For me, the word that comes closest to the state in which stress vanishes and creativity re-appears is the word "calm." This book, then, is about how to banish "un-calm" (stress) and replace it with un-stress (calm). My hope is that you will find it relaxing to read.

Stephen A. Schacher, M.D.
Athens, Georgia

DEDICATION

This book is dedicated to Paul D. MacLean, M.D., whose discovery of the Triune Brain is one of the great conceptual breakthroughs in science.

Contents

PART II

PART III

PART IV

INTRODUCTION

In case you haven't read the newspapers recently, watched TV, read national magazines, or listened to public officials discuss any topic whatsoever, let me briefly summarize what they have to say: "Everything is getting worse, and you should be worried sick about it all." You should be un-calm.

This, of course, is not only the opinion of the media and those in public office. In most private conversations that I hear, as well as those related to me by my patients, friends, relatives, and business relations, there is widespread agreement that everything is getting worse and has been deteriorating for quite a long time.

The cause of this seems to be politicians, government, the business sector, the socialist and capitalist points of view, the economy, the environment, all religions or the lack thereof, our educational institutions, the courts, the military and those who oppose the military.

On a personal level, the cause seems to be people's spouses, their children, their bosses, their relatives, their business associates, the unions, corporate management, financial institutions, the insurance industry, and government entitlements (either too many or too few).

Interestingly enough, things were a lot better before whoever is currently in power took office; before individuals either married, divorced, grew older, became ill, or were struck by unfortunate events; before they either took or lost their current job; or before someone did something very mean to them.

And for many people—though not all—there is a good chance that things will get better if only someone else gains control of the government; if they get divorced or married, quit their job or find a new one, get promoted or retire; if their children succeed more than they have (or simply move out); justice is done; or if they simplify or complicate their life further.

There is, however, one thing on which most people agree. More money wouldn't hurt! (although there are a few individuals who need _time_ more than they need money and a few others who need something—such as love—that money cannot buy).

i

For we know that the whole creation groans and suffers the pains of childbirth right up to the present time.[1]

A few days after I began the first draft of this book, TWA flight 800 crashed into the Atlantic following a mysterious on-board explosion. Everyone on board, including a high school French class from Pennsylvania, was killed. Prior to this, a lone gunman had massacred elementary school children in Drisbane, Scotland.

During the years that the book has taken shape, we have had on a national level the Columbine tragedy, the Beltway sniper incidents, and 9/11 with its significant aftermaths. Now we have the fear of global warming.

On personal levels, each of us can relate to family deaths, illnesses, and divisive arguments. All of these occur in the larger setting of our own sicknesses and mortality. We either die young, or we grow old and die. We lose loved ones or they lose us. Nothing is permanently ours; we cannot come to peace about money; love is elusive and, if found, can always be lost.

And yet, oddly enough, through it all, it is possible to have deep loves, great pleasures, satisfying moments, stimulating discussions, and uproarious fun. Life cannot be summed up, but the people who live it have one thing in common.

We all suffer from a permanent stress disorder called "life."

This book tries to remove the un-calm from all that. It is a reminder that stress has an opposite called relaxation, and others called satisfaction, fulfillment, creativity and happiness. It reminds us that life can be filled with courage instead of fear, joy instead of boredom, relationship instead of isolation, and faith instead of despair. It takes the position that in every situation, no matter how desperate, there is always something you can do that is far more satisfying than to "just be stressed." It is possible in every situation to remain calm.

In fact, as we will see, permitting the stress reaction to take you over, to make you un-calm, is the single worst choice you can make in any situation, no matter how desperate.

---

[1] *The Holy Bible.* Romans 8:22.

This book has four goals:

1. It will help you recognize when you are no longer calm and explain to you why you have become stressed.
2. It will give you the tools you need to respond to un-calm situations with a more interesting behavioral repertoire than simply running the stress reaction.
3. It will remind you to do those things—the opposites of stress—that lead to miraculous outcomes.
4. It will transform you from un-calm to calm.

PART I

THE ACUTE STRESS REACTION

OVERVIEW

CALM AND UN-CALM
We Cannot Avoid Stress

Most of us would like to be happy all of the time, and many of us do everything we can to make that possible. Yet, despite our best efforts, life and its problems just keep showing up on our doorstep. Some people blame the world; some people blame themselves; many people don't know whom to blame, although they are reasonably certain that there is someone who's behind it all. But until the day that the definitive solution comes along, life is likely to be sometimes positive (+), sometimes negative (-), and sometimes neutral (0) depending on the circumstances. You could envision it like this (Figure 1):

> **Example 1:** *Bob wakes up on Monday morning looking forward to making a great presentation at work to his boss. He has worked hard on this presentation and is confident it will win praise. He is in a state of pleasure, whistling to himself, and looking forward to the day at work (1). When he arrives at work, however, he discovers that the meeting has been cancelled. (2) He feels his happiness depart, and he becomes temporarily gloomy (3). He is a little irritable and short tempered with his staff without realizing it. He goes into his office, closes the door, and starts catching up on his e-mail. In a few minutes he is absorbed in work and forgets about the meeting and its cancellation (4).*

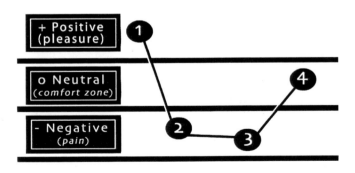

Figure 1

3

Scenarios like this happen repeatedly every day, and we find ourselves moving from happy states, to neutral states, to unhappy states and back again many times each day.

Generally we think of positive life experiences as pleasurable, negative life experiences as painful, and neutral life experiences as unnoticeable. In popular usage, the neutral life experiences are called our "comfort zone".

In general, people need no assistance at all when it comes to pleasure, and usually we are unaware of our inner state of being when we are in our comfort zone. But something definitely different and unpleasant occurs when we are in negative states. We become fearful or irritable. We lose patience with our work and with the people around us. We lose our calm. We become stressed.

As we will see throughout this book, once we are stressed, we try to get rid of this unpleasant feeling by attacking what we believe to be the source of the stress (fight), getting as far away from it as possible (flight), or playing dead, hoping it won't notice us and go away (freeze). See (Figure 2):

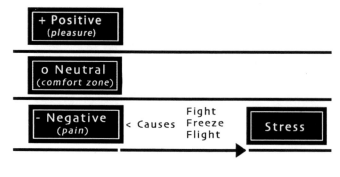

Figure 2

To avoid dealing with this kind of unpleasantness, some people try to remain in pleasure as much as possible, avoiding all pain, and distracting themselves endlessly—pretending that life has no problems. This is nearly impossible to accomplish, as life has many built-in problems for each us to confront, and sooner or later the pursuit of pleasure leads to its own stresses, since ignored problems simply grow larger and demand attention.

Exclusively pursuing pleasure inevitably leads to stress. This can happen for many reasons:

   i. Underestimating the need for safety.

    In skiing, motorcycling, mountain climbing or other potentially dangerous sports, in an attempt to increase pleasure, some individuals take more and more risks for the purpose of heightening pleasure until finally they exceed their ability and experience. At this point, they may find themselves in truly dangerous situations from which they may not be able to escape.

   ii. Underestimating basic biology.

    Cigarette smoking was a traditional pleasure enjoyed by many people, yet the biological consequences of this pleasure inducing activity eventually became apparent. Similarly, mind altering drugs, excessive alcohol and food intake, and the pleasure of inactivity can result in disease states which are quite stressful to experience. Failure to take into account the obvious reality of aging, because of an exclusive focus on the now, may also produce very stressful decades at the end of life.

   iii. Ignoring basic physics and chemistry:

    Wendy Northcutt has put together a series of amusing books[1] about people

---

[1] Northcutt, Wendy. *The Darwin Awards: Evolution in Action.* Plume Books. 2002.

who felt they could enjoy additional excitement and pleasure in life by daring to tread where others feared to go. Their ignorance of basic laws of chemistry and physics often led to their untimely demises (removing themselves from the gene pool and hence the name of her book—*The Darwin Awards*).

iv. Ignoring cultural and ethical boundaries:

Some people may attempt to increase their pleasure by crossing ethical or cultural boundaries (shoplifting, driving too fast, refusing to adapt to the mores of different cultures, or engaging in outright criminality). These activities generally plunge an individual into even more stress from having to confront the law and order side of life, as can be seen in (Figure 3):

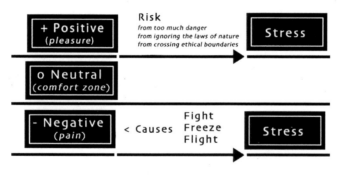

Figure 3

The Comfort Zone

Because painful circumstances lead to stress and the exclusive pursuit of pleasure can also lead to stress, many people seek to solve their stress problems by living a very low key life, avoiding both pleasure <u>and</u> pain. They attempt to remain at all times in their neutral comfort zones. To do this, they make their world very small and familiar. They choose to socialize only with the same friends, travel daily along the same familiar routes, vacation only at the same destinations, choose only familiar foods, and live their lives in predictable fashion.

For these individuals, life confronts them with boredom from insufficient novelty and exploration. These individuals discover that total predictability leads inevitably to boredom, and that surprisingly, boredom is also an immense stressor. See (Figure 4):

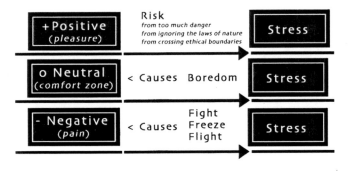

Figure 4

Attempts to live our lives free of stress by remaining fixed on pleasure, by avoiding all pain, or by avoiding all risk through living risk-free lives are all doomed to failure. Neither pleasure-seeking nor avoidance of life can keep us stress free. Sooner or later we have to learn to deal with un-calm.

There is no single, easy path to calm; but fortunately, it _is_ something that we can learn to achieve.

CHAPTER ONE

What Causes Un-calm?

Why do we ever lose our calm and become stressed? We lose our calm, because we cannot accommodate smoothly to the changes that occur in our lives.

A Few Definitions

For scientists every force that has an effect on us is called a <u>stressor</u>. These forces can be outside of us, such as a change in the weather or the mood of a family member, or they can be inside of us, such as a pain, an infection, a drop in our blood sugar, or an unpleasant memory. It really doesn't matter whether they are external or internal. What matters is that each one of these forces requires us to respond in some fashion. Not to respond is a characteristic of death, not life.

When these forces are very small, our bodies and minds <u>accommodate</u> (adjust to the new circumstance). This happens millions of times a day. Our blood sugar changes, our bodies accommodate. Someone says "Hello" in the work place, we respond appropriately. The accommodations our **bodies** make every day are collectively called <u>homeostasis</u> (literally, "same state"). The accommodations our **minds** make every day to routine life have no scientific name but are popularly called our <u>comfort zone</u>. Neither body homeostasis nor mental comfort zone adjustments cause us any stress.

However, anytime there is a slight increase in the force of the stressors acting on us, we move away from the safety of accommodation into stress. For example, your blood sugar might drop, and your mind realizes it is lunchtime. If it is a routine day, you know what you are going to do. This requires a little more effort than simple accommodation. You actually have to get up to go have lunch, but it is hardly an activity that will make you stressed.

But what if you suddenly remember that today's luncheon meeting is very important to you, or on the way to lunch you discover that you've forgotten your wallet at home, or just as you're leaving for lunch, an unexpected client walks in to meet with you.

If you are socially skilled and sophisticated, you have many learned behaviors that turn these potentially stressful situations into comfort zone non-problems. You can handle every one of them, practically without thinking. You have a wide comfort zone and can easily accommodate.

> **Example 1:** *But what if you can't. What if the unexpected client is very important to you but so is the luncheon? For a minute you may not be sure what to do. No solution seems perfect. At that moment of indecision, the moment at which you become un-calm, without even asking your permission, your body suddenly activates the complex cascade of hormones known collectively as the <u>acute stress reaction</u>.*

For a second you may become confused; you may even become irritable. Though you may be unaware of it, your heart rate has increased, and you may be sweating ever so slightly. Your breathing, totally unnoticed by you, has become shallower and more rapid. You may be a little short tempered with people around you. Your face is not relaxed, and neither is your body. You might accidentally knock over your coffee cup or pass by someone in the hall without your customary good-natured greeting. You might even leave the office without your car keys. You have succumbed to the *acute stress reaction*.

The Sudden Appearance of Acute Stress

The acute stress reaction is a chemical change that your body undergoes when your mind thinks you are in true danger. Interestingly, the danger can merely be to your ego or it can be extreme physical danger to your body. It can even be imagined danger.

Why we have something, which seems to be so inappropriate to our modern lives as the acute stress reaction, is a subject that we will cover in a little while. But for the moment, it is enough to know that anytime we are in a situation in which we have not learned what to do, the absurdly powerful stress reaction takes us over.

The problem with the stress reaction in most situations is that it appears to be based on the idea that we are in real physical danger and that we either have to fight our way out of it or flee from it as fast as we can. The powerful adrenal gland hormones released into our bodies prepare us for the famous "fight or flight reaction", giving us the conscious experience of anger or fear. In normal business and social situations, this makes us unnecessarily angry or afraid, and we usually overreact with far too much emotion. More importantly, the acute stress reaction diverts energy from the thinking parts of our brain to our muscles and emotional centers. We become fighting or fleeing machines. We lose our ability to think rationally.

In most situations, then, our first task is to stop the acute stress reaction, so that we can recover our ability to think clearly.

How to Make Stress Disappear

Although many people have learned that the first step in overcoming acute stress is to take a deep breath, there is actually a crucial step which precedes that. The most important thing to do <u>first</u> is to realize that you are having an acute stress reaction. Unless you can realize this, you won't know to take that deep breath.

- **Step 1: Realize you are having an acute stress reaction**. This takes lots and lots of practice, because the thinking or awareness part of your brain—the cerebral cortex —is having energy taken away from it and sent to the areas of emotion and automatic behavior. As a result you are not self-aware. When you finish this book, it will be second nature for you to be aware the moment you enter the acute stress reaction.

- **Step 2: Take a deep breath**. Breathing is a body activity that can be carried out either consciously (with awareness) or unconsciously (without awareness). When you take a deep breath with awareness, you begin to break the stress reaction. This permits you to start the process of regaining control of your body and mind.

- **Step 3: Prepare to go slower**: Actually, what works to stop the effects of adrenal hormones is to slow down, but if I tell someone to "Slow down!", the command itself makes them more stressed, and they will speed up. On the other hand, "prepare to slow down", by being a suggestion rather than a command, is experienced as non-threatening, and I have found that it works to slow people down.

- **Step 4: Widen your vision**. In stress, your eye muscles become rigid. They are unconsciously looking for either a way to escape from the apparent danger or to attack the cause of the stress. In other words, the muscles of the eyes are very tense. By widening your visual field, you will further break the stress reaction. I urge people to look around the room or go to a window and look at the horizon. Try to focus on something very far away or scan the horizon. Look up at the sky and from side to side, taking in as wide a visual field as possible. At this point, your cerebral cortex will once again be receiving blood flow, and you will be able to think.

If you are a person who believes in the power of prayer in stressful situations, this is a good point to insert your prayer. Prayer widens your mental outlook to the farthest regions of the universe and utilizes the thinking part of your brain. Clearly it encourages you that help is forthcoming.

- **Step 5: Loosen your jaw**: As you become aware of how your body tenses in acute stress, you will begin to notice that your jaw is one of those areas of muscle tension. The vocal cords also become tense, which is why people lose their voice in stage fright. Loosening (slightly opening) the jaw allows blood to flow back into your tongue and jaw and into your vocal cords as well.

- **Step 6: Discover the source of the stress**. With the body now more relaxed and the mind freed enough from stress so that it can think, the goal becomes to discover the source of the stress. In acute stress, this is usually very easy. In the example above, when the important client appears just as you are heading out for a lunch appointment, the source of the stress is two events competing for attention at the same time. Once the source of the stress is known, a solution is usually possible through communication. Communication always lowers stress, because stress is a type of separation from others, while good communication with others is always relaxing.

- **Step 7: Communicate with the source of the stress**: Once you have discovered the source of the stress, you will discover that most times communication with the source of the stress will eliminate the stress reaction. In the example, phoning the restaurant to tell your friend you will be late, communicating with the unexpected client that you can't see him now but can make an appointment with him for later, will probably resolve the stress. Although not every acute stress problem can be <u>solved</u> by communication, communication with the source of the stress reduces the stress in an amazing number of problems.

Note that I said communicating with the <u>source</u> of the stress is what reduces stress in most acute stress problems. This is different from communicating with just anyone who happens to be around. Many people ward off their nervousness in acute stress by talking to people who have nothing to do with either the problem or its solution. This is "complaining", and it is usually ineffective. People complain to others because they are frightened to talk to the source of the stress. It is hard to realize that this fear comes from the stress reaction itself and is not necessarily arising from fear of the other person. The key is to talk to the person who is the source of the stress.

Question: What if you can't communicate with the source of the stress, or the source of the stress refuses to communicate with you?

Answer: If the source of the stress won't communicate with you, the situation passes from acute stress to chronic stress. This is often the initial strategy of terrorists, of opposing sides in bitter disputes, and of people who wish to keep you in the dark. It is often a deliberate technique to raise stress rather than to lower it. The goal is to get back into communication, if possible, either directly or indirectly, through intermediaries. How to deal with chronic stress is described in Part II; for the moment, it would take us too far afield if discussed right here.

Question: What about acute stress problems where there is no one with whom to communicate—for example, when the problem is time?

Answer: Time is a relentless stressor, because there is no way to communicate with the source of time in order to get more when you need it or get rid of some when you have too much on your hands. But if you can break the stress reaction and communicate with someone who can change a deadline, then the stress of time can be relieved. I've noticed, however, that many people who are stressed by time, are actually stressed by their own **internal** sense of time—their perception that they don't have enough time for their needs—rather than by the true clock time available. Near the end of the book (Chapter 8), I discuss what it means to develop patience, the true antidote for time urgency. If time is a relentless stressor for you, you might enjoy reading that section first and then returning to this chapter.

The same ideas hold true for chronic pain. If doctors cannot communicate (through treatment) with the source of the pain, you have to experience its relentless misery. But if the source of pain can be found, most likely it can be relieved. So communicating (or discovering) the source of the stress is a crucial step towards its elimination. Many times, the source of the stress **can** be located with great effort, and when this happens, the reward is that the stress disappears. If not, the affected individual will pass into chronic stress.

Question; What if the source of the stress will communicate with you but not agree with you on the solution?

Answer: Sometimes, the source of the stress is obvious, but the solution is not. An example would be, "my father won't let me date the boy I want to date". In this case the source of the stress is something in the father's system of beliefs that clashes with something in the daughter's system of beliefs. If the two can communicate and work out the differences, they may be able to zero out the stress. If they cannot, the stress will linger as a chronic stress reaction.

Question: What if you can't figure out the source of the stress?

Answer: Sometimes the source of the stress is not obvious at all. You are a rising star in every company you work for, but once you reach a certain level, you make mistakes. The fact that you fail once you reach certain levels of responsibility is clear to you, but the cause is not. As we will see in the chapters on chronic stress and post-traumatic stress syndrome, finding the source of this stress may require professional help, because it may be so buried in the mind that it takes a skillful therapist to find it.

> **Example 2:** *A remarkable example of the effectiveness of the formula for breaking the acute stress reaction occurred to me about ten years ago. As I mentioned in the foreword, I used to give stress classes on Saturday mornings to my Internal Medicine patients in Seattle. I always looked forward to these classes and was very pleased with myself for offering them. One Saturday morning, I slept a little late and had to race to the office. When I arrived a few minutes late, a number of people were already waiting including patients who had brought guests. They were standing outside the office waiting for me. As I reached into my pocket, I realized that I had left the key to the office at home.*

I was embarrassed about being late and now doubly embarrassed by not having the key. I felt unprofessional. I was about to stammer an apology, when I had the good fortune to realize that I was having an acute stress reaction (**step 1, above**). I took a deep breath (**step 2**), slowed down (**step 3**) and explained the situation to my audience, including the fact that I—the teacher—was having the very thing we were going to study. I said I might as well use the formula I'd been teaching.

So I widened my vision (**step 4**) and looked toward the horizon. And there, at the far end of the parking lot, just about to drive off, was the building manager getting into his car. I shouted his name and waved, and he drove over to see what I needed. He had the key. It was lucky, but if I hadn't realized I was stressed, relaxed, and widened my vision, even that lucky opportunity would have passed me by.

Observing the Stress Reaction for Fun and Knowledge

It is crucial to understand the acute stress reaction, because even the chronic stress reaction is just the result of individual acute stress reactions that were never solved. What most people mean by "stress" is the lifetime accumulation of unsolved acute stress problems which they have never known how to solve and which have now become chronic stress problems. Superimposed on these are daily acute stress reactions, which continue to accumulate. Eventually people reach a point at which their ability to accommodate to all of these reactions at the same time (called "**coping ability**") is exceeded. When this occurs they seem to be in permanent stress and are very difficult to help. In fact, it becomes very hard to keep them calm enough to communicate with them.

Oddly enough, it is not that difficult to learn how to deal with acute and chronic stress and thereby increase your coping capacity. As coping capacity enlarges, life enjoyment returns and with it the pleasures that life has to offer.

There is a small amount of learning required to understand these reactions. Interestingly, learning itself is a stressor, as any student can tell you. When I gave my Saturday morning stress classes, I could watch the faces of those in attendance and discern by their facial expressions when enough new material had been presented. I tried to gauge when I should stop and ask for questions, lighten the mood with an anecdote, let them speak instead of me, and when to take a break.

I cannot see the faces of people reading this book, but I can tell you that if you take in too much material without a break to digest what you have learned, you will become bored and forget what you have just read. So, in reading this book, if you become bored, you should put it down until the desire to read it surfaces again. You will discover that just before you became bored, you had taken in enough new material. Your brain needs time to digest what you have already read.

At this point, let's take a break.

*   *   *   *   *

Awareness Training for Chapter 1

If you are a novice in learning about stress, stop here for a moment and spend some time observing yourself. Notice when you seem to be comfortable and when you seem to be stressed. Most people are slightly stressed most of the time—especially in public—so see if you can notice when you slip into stress yourself. Pay attention to your face muscles, especially your jaw, your breathing, and your posture. Are your muscles relaxed or slightly tense? How about your conversation and your voice? Are you actually listening to the person with whom you are conversing or are you on internal dialogue? How about your hands? Are they fidgeting or relaxed? What about your legs—nervously jiggling back and forth or comfortably aligned with gravity?

Are you stressed because you are bored?

If not, is your internal emotion either anger or fear (the two fundamental emotions of stress), or are you happy, excited, interested, and joyful? If you had to speak, would your voice be resonant or breathless and dry?

If you can learn to notice when you become stressed, take a deep breath, prepare to slow down, widen your vision, pray if you are so inclined, and loosen your jaw. Each of these actions will begin to relax you (by breaking the stress reaction) and give you an opportunity to communicate with the source of the stress. It doesn't have to happen immediately. However, once you can stop the stress reaction, something <u>remarkable</u> happens:

As you become calm, <u>you</u> become someone with whom it is easy to communicate. As a result, instead of having to look for the source of the stress, the source of the stress may find you and begin to communicate. It could be that in <u>their</u> universe, the source of the stress is you!

Chapter Two

The Biological Basis of Un-calm

I am hoping that you have had a chance to observe yourself during acute stress reactions since reading Chapter 1. If not, be patient, but try to become self-aware. Becoming aware of stress in oneself may take some time to achieve, because self-awareness is lost during stress. If you did manage to notice being stressed, you probably also noticed that at <u>the exact</u> moment you became aware of being stressed, the stress reaction began to lose its grip on you. This is because the stress reaction is always an unaware activity, and the moment you make it conscious, it loses its steam. In this next session, we will learn the nuts and bolts of why this is so.

If at any point in reading the book, you find your attention wandering, feel free to put it down until you feel like picking it up again—or browse through other parts of the book. I want you to be relaxed while reading it. Our brains just can't absorb new material, if they are in distress.

Why do we have stress?

There are two very odd things about the acute stress reaction:
  i. <u>It is far more powerful than is needed for most situations that activate it</u>. We really don't have to react to a lost contact lens, a friend who is late for an appointment, or a traffic jam on the highway, as though we were being attacked by a herd of wild animals. Yet, once we are stressed, this is what happens.
  ii. The second odd thing about it is <u>that the very skills we need</u> for responding to stressful situations, namely, a cool head and good communication skills, <u>are the exact skills which the acute stress reaction takes away from us</u>.

How this has occurred is fun to speculate. If you are an evolutionist, you might say that we have inherited the basic animal survival skills of our evolutionary ancestors without being given the less frantic updates that our more developed and more communicative brains would find useful. If so, someone is asleep at the wheel at the Evolution Software Company.

On the other hand, if you are a Creationist, you might say that we are edgy and fearful because our separation from God following the Fall has made us feel fearful and alone in the Universe.

Regardless of the reason, the fact remains that we have hardwired[1] into our brains something which is far more powerful and strangely misdirected than the behaviors we need in our present day lives. Let's look behind the curtain.

We Have a Triune Brain

There is an extraordinarily useful description of how the human brain works that was created by Paul MacLean, M.D.[2] after a lifetime of scientific research. It is called the <u>triune</u> (means: "3 part") <u>brain</u>, and the concepts and terminology associated with it have won wide acceptance among biologists. Even though here and there researchers have found exceptions to the model, the fundamental explanation it provides of how the human brain works is a masterpiece of making the complex more easily understood. As you will see, it cracks open the problem of acute stress so simply, it becomes non-stressful to learn about it.

---

[1] By hardwired, I mean it is a result of the way the brain is built not the result of our thoughts or moods. As a result, we have no direct control over the stress reaction.
[2] MacLean, P.D. *The Triune Brain in Evolution*. Plenum Press. 1990.

MacLean, who had studied the brains of reptiles, mammals, and humans, noted that the human brain could be understood as though there were a reptilian brain at its center, covered by a mammalian brain, and this in turn by a human brain. (See Figure 5.) What we are going to learn is that the acute stress reaction is primarily a property of the reptilian brain. This is why the stress reaction seems to be something that our primitive ancestors needed for survival [fight or flight] but that we, with our sophisticated abilities at communication, have seemingly outgrown.

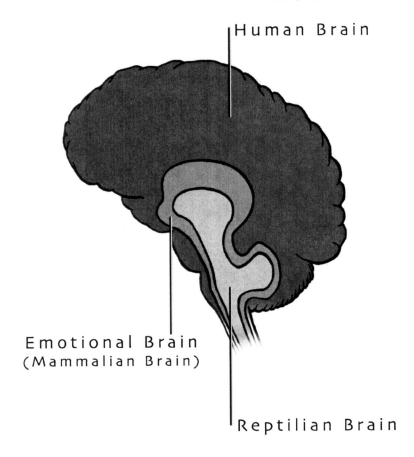

Human Brain

**Emotional Brain
(Mammalian Brain)**

Reptilian Brain

Figure 5

The Reptilian Brain

The reptilian brain consists of a variety of structures at the base of the brain which govern our most basic internal mechanisms, such as control of blood pressure, metabolism, growth, and sexual activity; instinctual behaviors such as foraging for food and hoarding it for later use; grooming, marking and defending a territory, defining social hierarchies, greeting, courtship and mating; and collective behaviors such as migrating and flocking. **The stress reaction is hard wired into the reptilian brain**.

> ***Example 1:*** <u>An example of reptilian behavior</u>: *Here is a paraphrase of a description of reptilian behavior from MacLean. It will look and sound familiar to us humans, as reminiscent of our own behavior in certain circumstances. I have called the main reptilian character Rex for ease in reading.*

An intruding male lizard has approached to within 15 feet of a woodpile, which is home territory to another male lizard, Rex. Tension is rising, as the intruder continues to invade.

Rex stops what he's doing. He elevates himself to the highest point of the woodpile. where he begins a series of menacing displays. He turns sideways to display his great size and strength. Undaunted, the young lizard moves ever forward, replying with his own displays of aggression.

Rex's female companion comes out of the woodpile with one of her females-in-waiting to observe the combat. Rex dares the young lizard to advance. Suddenly, the young lizard accepts the challenge and crosses the critical threshold. The battle is engaged.

Rex leaps down from the top display post and heads straight for the intruder. Just as he seems about to collide with him, Rex rises up on all fours. Like all territorial males, he emphasizes his ferocity by alternately flexing and extending all four extremities. With his nuchal crest (back of the neck) elevated, his gular fold (Adam's apple) extended, and his body flattened, he looks particularly menacing, especially when seen from the side.

The intruder panics and a chase ensues. Rex runs the intruder off his territory. Having dispensed of a younger rival, Rex returns to his top display post and proclaims his victory by three head bobs.[3] He is still "king of the hill".

In this description of reptilian behavior we have all the elements of the human acute stress reaction:

- Something has occurred which has pushed the organism in question (Rex) out of his comfort zone.
- The stress reaction has been activated.
- Fight or flight[4]—in this case, fight—ensues.
- There is a brief struggle for dominance, a winner is declared, the loser flees, and the emergency is over.
- The acute stress reaction has ended.

We can see humans engaged in reptilian behavior perfectly in professional wrestling matches. The two combatants appear as champions, enlarging their actual size by puffing up their chests, by posturing, flexing, strutting, and utilizing cocksure head movements. They are accompanied by a fawning retinue, whose purpose is to transmit awe. No time is wasted on communication, except to verbally challenge the other side. The goal is to threaten, to increase stress, to dominate, and to avoid being dominated.

---

[3] Ibid. pgs. 119-120.
[4] I have only alluded to fight or flight indirectly so far. I will explain it in detail very soon.

Interestingly, what is done for entertainment in wrestling is done for deadly serious purposes in human warfare. We all instinctually understand what is going on in these struggles, because we all share this reptilian brain system.

Please remember as we proceed. The acute stress reaction is hard wired into the <u>reptilian</u> portion of our brains. This is the level at which we function, when we are stressed.

The Mammalian Brain

The mammalian brain is that part of our brain which controls our emotions and our emotional memories.

It is no accident that the mammalian brain is the one in which emotions first appear. Mammals are the first organisms in the ladder of biological complexity who nurse their young, in whom maternal-offspring bonding first appears, and in whom play between parents and offspring (and between siblings) is observable[5]. Thus the development of mammals parallels the development of the family, and it is in this setting that **emotions and emotional memory** make their first appearance[6].

This is why, when we recall certain events, we also recall the emotions associated with them. A familiar example of this is found in arguments between couples, whether married or dating. At some point in the argument, if it is intense enough, one or both of the partners will begin to recall a long list of disappointments or upsets supposedly linked to the current argument. From the point of view of content, these remembered events are often completely unrelated to the immediate point of contention, with one

---

[5] Ibid, Page 247.
[6] A fascinating book on animal emotions is *When Elephants Weep: The Emotional Lives of Animals*, by Masson, J.M. and McCarthy, S. Delacorte Press. 1995.

exception. They are linked by the similarity of the emotions they evoked.

The other partner may be at a loss to know how an incident that occurred 15 years previous is linked to the present incident. The answer is not that the two incidents are similar in what happened, but rather that they are similar in how they made the individual feel. Listen to people tell a series of stories that wander from one subject to another, as they make random associations, and you will notice that the thread is an emotional one.

Mammals organize their memories by smell as well as by emotion, since so much of their world is organized by odors. Humans have nowhere near the heightened sense of smell that other mammals do, but we retain the ability to file memories by smell. There is one famous example that links the human sense of smell to emotional memories. Nineteenth century French author, Marcel Proust, wrote an extraordinarily long book about his childhood memories, *Remembrance of Things Past*. These memories are very rich, filled with all the emotions he felt at the time. As is well known, they were triggered by the smell of a butter cookie he had loved in childhood, the "madeleine".

Scientists refer to the "mammalian brain" as **the limbic lobe** of the brain (see Figure 6), and that is how I will refer to it from now on.

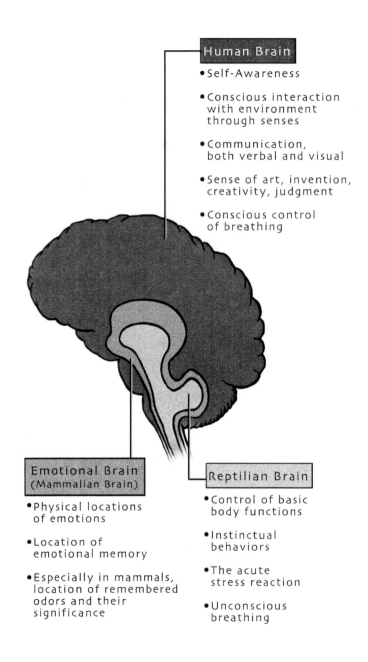

Human Brain
- Self-Awareness
- Conscious interaction with environment through senses
- Communication, both verbal and visual
- Sense of art, invention, creativity, judgment
- Conscious control of breathing

Emotional Brain
(Mammalian Brain)
- Physical locations of emotions
- Location of emotional memory
- Especially in mammals, location of remembered odors and their significance

Reptilian Brain
- Control of basic body functions
- Instinctual behaviors
- The acute stress reaction
- Unconscious breathing

Figure 6

The Human Brain (the cerebral cortex)

The human brain consists of what we have called the reptilian brain, surrounded by the limbic lobe (mammalian brain), and these, in turn, are surrounded by the gigantic **cerebral cortex** of humans. In mammals, the cerebral cortex is relatively small. In humans the cerebral cortex has increased massively in size. It seems to be what makes us human. It is the home of all conscious awareness; of language, of communication, of reasoning and planning; of visualization, art, and creativity; of our voluntary muscle control, of our eyesight, sensory abilities, and hearing; of our interpretations of what we see, hear and feel; of our imagination; of our religious and ethical senses; and it is the repository of our ideas about God. The cerebral cortex is the home of everything we think to be uniquely human.

What is it that makes the human brain different from the reptilian and mammalian brains? More that anything else it is communication—verbal communication (words), visual communication (symbols, drawings, mental images), musical communication (songs and rhythms), and self-awareness (communication with oneself, thinking, and inner dialogue).

It is true that reptiles and mammals communicate, but humans do it continually with words, pictures, music, symbols, and inner dialogue. Although there is good evidence that chimps (and perhaps other species) have some self-awareness, in humans, self-awareness—the sense of "I"—is fundamental to who we are. In fact, it is because of this highly developed sense of "I" that we can imagine and become afraid of death. Because of this sense of "I", humans have moral dilemmas and questions about the source of existence.

Despite the addition of these extraordinarily sophisticated communication and self-awareness systems, when it comes to stress, humans do what reptiles and mammals do; they make their new abilities subservient to the overriding demands of previous abilities. In other words, our magnificent communicative cerebral cortex can be at the mercy of our reptilian brain, *if we let it*. And this is exactly what happens in the stress reaction. We either have to use our cerebral cortex to break the stress reaction, or fail to use it and succumb to the reptilian mind. An example will make the point.

> **Example 3:** *It is Friday evening and you have just come home. You stop at the mailbox. There are letters, bills, and junk mail. One is from the Acme Gidget Company, and it catches your eye. You wonder why it is there. You open it and discover that you were charged for having purchased a gidget by phone solicitation. You remember very clearly having told the caller that you didn't want the gidget, yet in your hands is a bill claiming you ordered it.*

Just seeing the bill (this overwhelms the cortex) has made you instantly furious (emotions from the limbic lobe). That in turn has reflexively activated the stress reaction (from the reptilian brain). You are now in reptilian mode—fight or flight, dominate or be dominated. In this case, you are in fight. You rush to the telephone to target the hapless flak catcher at the Acme Gidget Company with your wrath. But, alas! It's Friday evening, and they're closed until Monday. You are filled with rage, with circulating noradrenalin, tense muscles, a protruded jaw, and a pounding heart. Yet there is no one appropriate on whom to vent your rage.

You look around in turmoil and frustration and notice that once again your son, daughter, or spouse has left a wet towel on the new carpet. How many times have you asked them not to do that? Are you made of money? Does anyone care about how hard you work? You see your family, and you explode—not just with the minor frustration of the towel upset, but also with the full pent up rage of the unfair charge on your credit card bill. By now, your anger has become hooked up (via the limbic lobe) to numerous other free-floating frustrations of the day, the week, the year, and your life. The beautiful, sophisticated human communication system, with its elegant verbal, visual, and musical skills has become a slave to the limbic memory system (linking things by emotion), and that in turn has reflexively activated the reptilian stress system.

Reptilian "fight or flight"—destroy the enemy or surrender—has taken over from "communicate your thoughts and feelings to another highly developed individual". The human brain has become subservient to the mammalian and reptilian brains. With noradrenalin surging, it will be quite some time before you can calm down.

How Our Bodies Change from Stress to Relaxation

We now have all the building blocks in place to understand the acute stress reaction. Figure 7 shows the triune brain in stress. The cerebral cortex has essentially ceased to function and the limbic (emotional) system is under the direct control of the reptilian brain.

Figure 8 shows the triune brain as it emerges from stress. The cerebral cortex is once again in control and has reined in the emotional system. The reptilian brain has become subservient to the cortex rather than in control of it.

The Triune Brain in Stress

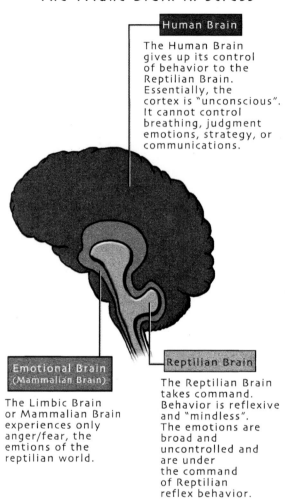

Human Brain

The Human Brain gives up its control of behavior to the Reptilian Brain. Essentially, the cortex is "unconscious". It cannot control breathing, judgment emotions, strategy, or communications.

Emotional Brain (Mammalian Brain)

The Limbic Brain or Mammalian Brain experiences only anger/fear, the emtions of the reptilian world.

Reptilian Brain

The Reptilian Brain takes command. Behavior is reflexive and "mindless". The emotions are broad and uncontrolled and are under the command of Reptilian reflex behavior.

Stress

- *Reptilian brain in charge.*
- *Cortex is silent.*
- *Limbic lobe experiences only anger/fear, the emotions of the reptilian world.*

Figure 7

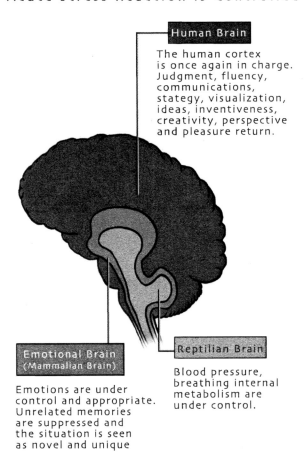

The Triune Brain After the Acute Stress Reaction is Controlled

Human Brain

The human cortex is once again in charge. Judgment, fluency, communications, stategy, visualization, ideas, inventiveness, creativity, perspective and pleasure return.

Emotional Brain (Mammalian Brain)

Emotions are under control and appropriate. Unrelated memories are suppressed and the situation is seen as novel and unique

Reptilian Brain

Blood pressure, breathing internal metabolism are under control.

Non-stress

- *Cerebral cortex in charge.*
- *Reptilian brain is under conscious control.*
- *Limbic lobe can experience any emotion.*

Figure 8

Awareness Training Chapter 2

There is a lot of new material in this chapter, if you've never heard it before. I suggest you put the book down and spend some time becoming familiar with the triune brain concept. It is possible that you will now enjoy "irrational arguments" that you overhear or are involved in. The participants are hooking things together by emotion not reason. Instead of these disputes making you crazy with their illogic, you may find that they are fascinating, now that you have the key.

You may also be able to catch yourself when you get overly angry or frightened by an insignificant event and realize that you have opened an emotional bin in your limbic lobe. Once you realize this, you might enjoy discovering which events are linked together in your mind by emotion. If you can enjoy observing yourself, you will have engaged your cerebral cortex, and the stress reaction will fade away.

Chapter Three

The Repetitious Behaviors of Stress

Whenever you are calm, it is natural to want to participate in life. This can take the form of conversation with others, reading, writing, creating, playing sports, engaging in hobbies and crafts, watching entertainment, daydreaming, learning or carrying out any other activity that engages your human mind. But when you are stressed, you are only angry, afraid, or panicked and you only want to fight, hide, or run away.

Stress behavior is amazingly stereotyped, and it makes for a very repetitious life. Calm behavior is amazingly varied, and it makes for a very full life. Unfortunately, it takes almost no effort at all to fall into stress; your reptilian brain will do it for you. On the other hand, it takes a lot of effort and training to remain calm, and you need to use your human brain to make it happen.

Stress: A Reptilian Solution to Life's Problems

As we saw in Chapter 1, our brains will trigger the acute stress reaction in any situation in which our cerebral cortex (our human brain) discovers that it doesn't know what to do. If we can keep a cool head in these situations (that is, prevent our reptilian brain, with its limited repertoire, from taking over our emotional system), we may be able to figure out a successful strategy for confronting our problem. This strategy almost always includes some form of communication, because that is what the human cerebral cortex does best. People who can handle a wide range of problems without becoming stressed are said to have good **coping ability**, and later (Part II) we will see how some expert copers developed their abilities.

Whenever we cannot cope (cannot keep our emotions under control), our reptilian brain sits in the driver's seat. The reptilian brain has as its prime directive, "dominate! and if that fails, then at all costs avoid being dominated!"

When I first learned about stress, this reptilian stress reaction was called "the fight or flight reaction", meaning that the individual in its grip either attacks the source of the stress or attempts to escape from it. However, a common observation is that many people become "paralyzed" with fear—that is, in the midst of danger, they just stand there and shake or run around hysterically, neither fighting nor fleeing. This is also consistent with reptilian behavior. Some snakes and other reptiles respond to stress by "playing dead", which is neither fight nor flight, but a strategy aimed at survival. So to really understand stress, we have to realize that the reptilian options are fight, run away, or play dead, which I call fight, flee, or freeze.

What "fight, flee, or freeze" means is that when an organism is acutely stressed (placed in a situation in which it doesn't know what to do) that organism will either run as far as possible away from the source of the stress (escape), stay still and tremble, or turn and attack the source of the stress with the intention of destroying it. These are the reptilian solutions to discomfort, and we use them all reflexively.

When we are stressed, it is our reptilian brain that is activated. Like reptiles and mammals, people will do anything to lower their stress. That is how powerful and unconscious the stress reaction is. Since ethics is stored in the human part of our brain, not in our reptilian brain, it takes a lot of self awareness and immense self-control to stay ethical as the stress increases.

Responding to Stress: Fight, Flight or Freeze

What seems to determine whether fight, flight, or freeze will take place in humans or animals is the instantaneous assessment by any threatened organism as to whether it thinks it will win or lose if conflict occurs.[1] If it believes it cannot win, it will engage either in escape from the stress or play dead (which is actually surrender). If it believes it can win, it will engage in aggression. In either event, the goal is to lower the stress.

The Pluses and Minuses of Fight

If an organism decides to fight, the body's energy is directed outward and upward, from the center of the body where the organs of digestion and elimination are found to the periphery of the body where the skeletal muscles are located. The emotional centers in the brain are activated for rage, and the special senses (vision, smell, and hearing) become more acute. (See Figure 9):

---

[1] A book that emphasizes this exact moment of decision is *Learned Optimism* by Martin Seligman, Ph.D.

In fight, energy is directed into the muscles of the upper body. The legs stiffen to hold their position.The eyes are targeted at the stressor. The jaw protrudes. The chest is hyper-inflated. The hands may fill with energy and form a fist. The voice is louder, speech is shortened and barked. Vocabulary and sentence structure simplify (due to less cerebral cortex input).

The legs stiffen, the buttocks contract and tilt the pelvis forward, the feet grip the ground firmly.

Heart rate and blood pressure increase. There is an increase in blood flow to the muscles. Blood coagulation is more rapid (possibly to prevent surface bleeding from injuries). Body temperature rises.

The stressed individual in fight is seeking to destroy the source of the stress, and if courageous enough, will shorten the distance between him or her and the stressor.

If it is socially inappropriate to actually attack, the individual may become stuck in acute stress (fight) resulting in neck and upper backaches, jaw pain, high blood pressure, headaches, staccato type speech, and an angry facial expression.

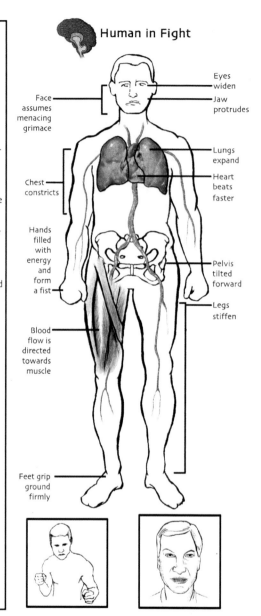

Human in Fight

Eyes widen

Jaw protrudes

Face assumes menacing grimace

Chest constricts

Hands filled with energy and form a fist

Blood flow is directed towards muscle

Feet grip ground firmly

Lungs expand

Heart beats faster

Pelvis tilted forward

Legs stiffen

Figure 9

In fight, the skeletal muscles become charged with energy under the action of noradrenalin[2]. The legs either stand their ground or move forward. The upper body is charged with energy for aggressive use of the arms, jaw, and teeth. The upper body grows larger as the lungs expand, the heart beats faster and more powerfully, the eyes widen and fix on their target, and the fists clench. The organism will usually take an aggressive, forward leaning stance and seek to close the distance to its target. The face assumes a menacing grimace. The voice deepens and booms louder. In mammals, there is a growl or a roar. The mind quickens, and thinking is focused on harming the opponent. The core of our being—the spirit—focuses on dominance and victory.

The positives: Successful athletes and winning armies use this energy to their advantage. Dominant athletes use the leg steadying and upper body enhancing effects to intimidate their opponents. Tennis players who feel dominant may serve exceptionally well at the crucial moment of the match; baseball pitchers may become harder to hit; fighters may be harder to knock down; and soccer players find their legs growing stronger. Target shooters notice their distant vision enhanced.

> **Example 1:** *I once read a story about Rod Laver, the outstanding Australian tennis champion, which took place when he was a teenager. According to the story, there were other 12 and 13-year-old tennis players who were better than he was, and who could beat him on the practice courts. But at about age 13, when they began to play in front of crowds, Laver's game became steadier and bolder, while the other players became more tentative and lost their edge. The stress reaction of playing in public produced the appropriate amount of fight in Laver but produced fear and flight in the others. Laver used the stress energy successfully; the others were thrown off their game by it. In them, flight rather than fight was energized.*

---

[2] Although the stress reaction is usually described as being caused by the powerful hormone adrenalin, in fact, it is another adrenal hormone, noradrenalin, that is actually the responsible agent.

The negatives: People who routinely carry anger just below the surface (that is, who are "angry at the world") are at risk for anger explosions with any provocation. These individuals develop chronic stress in their muscles of aggression. Their face always looks angry. Their shoulders, neck, and upper body are under continual tension, creating neck aches and headaches. The continuous circulation of noradrenalin creates high blood pressure, elevates cholesterol, and increases the risk for heart attacks and strokes. These are the original Type A personalities, first described by Rosenman and Friedman in their classic book, *Type A Behavior and Your Heart*.[3] Continual anger wears down the body and can lead to early death.

The Pluses and Minuses of Flight

In flight, energy moves away from the inner core organs and into the skeletal muscles, but this time the energy moves underscore{downwards} towards the legs, activating the powerful muscles of running. The lower body gains energy, the upper body loses energy. The face becomes frightened, the eyes become undercharged, the mind turns away from the stressor and looks into the distance for an escape. The individual abandons any idea of dominance and will probably submit, if he cannot escape. To confront is to risk greater harm than to run. It is only when escape has been successfully accomplished that the mind can regain calm and attempt to formulate a plan. (See Figure 10)

---

[3] Friedman, M. and Rosenman, R. *Type A Behavior and Your Heart*. Alfred A, Knopf. New York. 1974

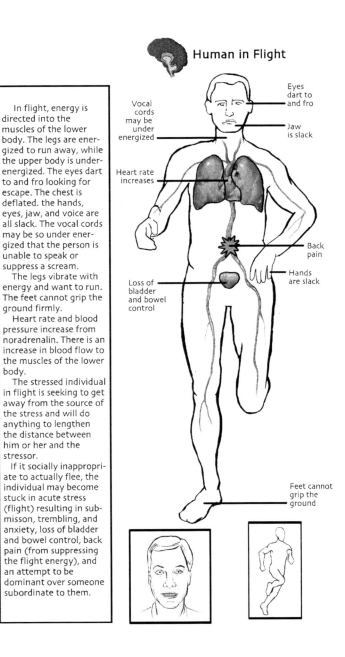

Human in Flight

In flight, energy is directed into the muscles of the lower body. The legs are energized to run away, while the upper body is under-energized. The eyes dart to and fro looking for escape. The chest is deflated. the hands, eyes, jaw, and voice are all slack. The vocal cords may be so under energized that the person is unable to speak or suppress a scream.

The legs vibrate with energy and want to run. The feet cannot grip the ground firmly.

Heart rate and blood pressure increase from noradrenalin. There is an increase in blood flow to the muscles of the lower body.

The stressed individual in flight is seeking to get away from the source of the stress and will do anything to lengthen the distance between him or her and the stressor.

If it socially inappropriate to actually flee, the individual may become stuck in acute stress (flight) resulting in submisson, trembling, and anxiety, loss of bladder and bowel control, back pain (from suppressing the flight energy), and an attempt to be dominant over someone subordinate to them.

Eyes dart to and fro

Jaw is slack

Vocal cords may be under energized

Heart rate increases

Back pain

Hands are slack

Loss of bladder and bowel control

Feet cannot grip the ground

Figure 10

41

The positives: Although flight is not as glamorous as fight, it is usually better to escape from danger than to succumb to it through underestimation of the threat.

The negatives: The biggest problem with "reptilian" flight is that in the absence of thinking, individuals sometimes mindlessly run into worse danger than the one from which they are fleeing. The better alternative is to realize the danger, break the stress reaction, and then—if escape is the most sensible option—escape consciously.

Choking: Because energy leaves the upper body and overcharges the lower body in flight, athletes who have a strong fear reaction near the end of a match may "choke." In this set of events, the legs are highly charged and may shake with energy, while the upper body is undercharged. Arms and upper back lose their strength, and the vocal cords lose their energy. This produces the famous squeaky voice of fear and gives "choking" its name.

Stage fright exhibits all of these features, and inexperienced actors may find themselves with no voice and shaking legs. Suitors asking for dates and employees asking for raises may have similar experiences. Tennis players with undercharged arms may lose their serve, while baseball pitchers may become "wild". Soccer players with overcharged legs may kick the ball over the net during a tie-breaking shoot out.

If fear is intense enough, the surge of energy to the lower body can result in the involuntary loss of bladder and bowel contents, an intensely embarrassing event in humans, but a common and possibly protective reaction in mammals.

Unusual Variations of Flight

Both mammals and humans grow bolder as they run away from danger and the distance between themselves and the source of the stress increases. In such circumstances, a mammal may stop running, turn around, and growl, because with the increased distance from the stressor, it feels bolder. Energy may return to its upper body, and some aggressive facial gestures may appear. In other words, as the stress decreases, the mammal may transform from flight back into fight.

Humans act similarly. Leaders who have been bested in battle may retreat in fear. When the distance from the danger source lengthens, and they have returned to a safer environment, their aggression may return. In the safer environment, the circulating noradrenalin now is re-directed from stimulating flight to stimulating fight, and the leader may order the troops to perform arduous and meaningless chores, simply to re-experience dominance.

The wage earner who returns home defeated from his or her day may immediately begin yelling at everyone over whom he or she has any authority. All of these reveal that fight and flight use the same energy (noradrenalin), the crucial difference between them being whether victory or defeat is perceived.

Who Responds with Fight?

Unlike stressful fight and flight, which are essentially out of our conscious control, skilled individuals who can break the stress reaction become more effective fighters. For example, some individuals have learned to hide when frightened, not just run away. Once safely hidden, they feel less stressed, and this permits them to become aggressive again. Instead of directly confronting their enemy, these individuals may attempt to fight a guerrilla action, sabotage enemy facilities, and disseminate misinformation to confuse the enemy. They may attempt to destroy enemy morale with terrorist raids. They are using fight and flight as conscious strategies.

Using the human brain rather than the reptilian brain creates an infinite variety of presentations. Fight can be everything from sarcasm to deadly attack. Sources of stress can be overpowered from a position of strength or whittled away slowly over a prolonged period through repeated attacks. Conscious fighting includes such varied strategies as direct attack, displays of overwhelming strength, the formation of alliances, attacks by intermediaries, or a commitment to continual hostility. Attempts to undermine the stressor include reducing its size and prestige with mockery, belittling, gossip, lies, and false rumors; dividing and conquering by breaking away small groups from the main force through threats, intimidation, and covert alliances; infiltrating its organization with spies and "third" columns; or turning public or world opinion against it.

Nationally and internationally, the entire science of war, politics, and dirty tricks clearly fall within the province of conscious fighting. Building alliances and coalitions, spying, propaganda, and saber rattling are all variations of fight. But even in conscious fighting, the goal remains to dominate (while avoiding being dominated)—the goals of our reptilian brains.

Others Take Flight

Skilled individuals can utilize consciousness in flight as well. Escape can include feigned madness (e.g. Hamlet or King David) or escape from the rules of society (as in cheating and criminality). There is also escape into silence or refusal to engage in meaningful communication. Watching television, reading, or just being unavailable (when done to avoid communication during difficult situations), all fall within the province of flight.

Less successful, partially conscious escape activities include escape into alcohol and drugs and escape into physical illness (malingering). Finally, although all suicides are not necessarily flight, there is escape into death through suicide or through forcing others to be the agents of one's death. An example of the latter would be the person who creates an intense situation, such as the taking of hostages, and then forces the police to kill him in order to free the hostages.

Many Panic or Freeze

Recently, as a result of research on a part of the mammalian brain (limbic lobe) called the <u>amygdala</u> (see Part IV), it has become apparent that there are 2 variations of flight that arise when certain centers of the brain are stimulated by the stress reaction. These two centers are the "freeze" and "appeasement" centers, both of which are variants of flight but with slightly different behaviors attached to them. "Freeze" is seen throughout the animal world and is a variant of shock. Reptiles, especially snakes, are reflexively wired to go into motionlessness when under attack or when covered by the shadow of an animal (usually a bird) that preys upon them. Humans also will freeze when threatened, if the fear generated is great enough.

Oddly, there is another center in the brain which when stimulated will cause the organism to seek appeasement. Humans who have trained animals will recognize this behavior as submission to authority. Humans display the same behavior with each other when in the presence of an overwhelmingly dominant authority.

Awareness Training Chapter 3

I mentioned earlier that the first step in controlling your stress is to recognize when you are in its grip. It is only then that you can breathe to break the stress reaction, widen your vision to engage the cerebral cortex, and seek to communicate to terminate the stress process. But since the attention of the mind reflexively abandons the human (cerebral) cortex during acute stress and takes up residence in the mammalian (limbic lobe) and reptilian portions of the brain, it takes training to recognize when you are stressed.

This training involves noticing when you are anywhere on the anger spectrum (from irritable to furious) or anywhere on the fear spectrum (from shy to terrified).

As an exercise, try to create a new reflex in yourself. Notice when you are suddenly angry or afraid and say "That's the stress reaction!" You notice that you are angry ... (SNAP!)... you realize that you are stressed. You're irritable ... (SNAP!)... you're stressed. Your boss or spouse is yelling...(SNAP!)... they're stressed!

Similarly with fear. You sense a shiver of fear ... (SNAP).... you're stressed. You want to run away or hide ... (SNAP)... you're stressed. You lose your voice, your mouth feels dry ... (SNAP) ... you're stressed.

When you sense anger or fear, notice it, breathe, widen your vision, pray if you are so inclined, prepare to slow down, and stay aware.

If you continue to observe yourself in these situations of anger and fear, you will notice that during times of stress you are unavailable for incoming communications, because your human brain has been hijacked by your reptilian brain. If you were a computer, you would have one of those little clocks or hourglasses on your forehead that computers use to signal when they are not available for input. When you succeed in making the acute stress reaction disappear, you will be available once again for incoming communications.

When people are on internal, their eyes usually drift off axis and instead of looking at you, they are slightly not looking at anything. If I notice that in another person, I usually slow my speech or stop communicating entirely, because they are not available for input. When their eyes return to axis, I start up again. (If they were thinking about what you just said and are not mentally absent, they will let you know.)

Stress for Fun

I can't leave the topic of the acute stress reaction without mentioning "stress for fun."

> **Example 2:** *Their hearts are pounding; their palms are sweaty. Their eyes are widened in fear. A scream is forming in their throat. They want to run, but they can't. They can't speak, only stammer. What can these poor stress victims do? Should they breathe, widen their vision, or slow down? Should they communicate with the source of the stress? Or… should they… (gasp) just … enjoy it.*

Yes, movie fans across the globe are using their wonderful reptilian stress systems for pure pleasure—watching horror movies, adventure stories, dangerous spy adventures, and wild automobile chases. They are joined in this by sports fans nearly fainting from excitement as the game winds down to its final seconds with the score tied. Other thrill seekers are paying real money—sometimes a lot—to ski down dangerous terrains, climb sheer cliffs, go into free fall on huge roller coasters, jump out of airplanes, or fall into ravines on bungee cords. Is this really the same stress reaction as the one that produces utter terror because of a lost contact lens or lost theater tickets?

Oddly enough it is. The same brain cells that bring you sweaty palms before a big interview bring you those same sweaty palms before the Super Bowl. What's the difference? Why is one painful and the other so pleasurable?

The answer is that during the Super Bowl or other exciting events, you <u>consciously</u> anticipate pleasure (via your cerebral cortex), and you know exactly what this pleasure feels like. You may not be in complete control of how you feel, but being conscious and in a state of pleasure, you are reaching towards the event. The fight/flight system is on, but so is the cerebral cortex. In stress, the fight/flight system is on, but the cerebral cortex is not. It has abandoned its role to the reptilian brain.

> **Example 3:** *Imagine you have just lost tickets to an event that you paid a lot of money to see. You are in a state of pain. You lose conscious control of your emotions. The reptilian fight/flight/freeze system has suddenly hijacked your emotional system and sent you into acute stress...I assume by now that you know what to do.*

SUMMARY

Part I: Calm and Un-calm

1. Every force that acts on an organism is called a <u>stressor</u>.
2. Most stressors are handled by either the body or the mind <u>accommodating</u> to them. They do not activate the <u>stress reaction</u>.
3. All stressors that do not activate the stress response fall within an individual's <u>comfort zone</u>.
4. Stressors that push an individual outside of his or her comfort zone may activate the stress reaction.
5. When the stress reaction is activated, the human cortex gives up its control of behavior to a less behaviorally complex portion of the brain called the "reptilian brain". This area of the brain tends to react to discomfort with "fight, flight or freeze"—the universal stress reaction. This switch from human brain control to reptilian brain control occurs <u>without conscious awareness.</u> It is pure reflex. The reptilian brain then takes over the mammalian emotional system, leading to the emotions of stress (anger or fear).
6. Because we do not realize what has happened, the full-blown acute stress reaction, with all of its consequences, is activated.
7. To break free from the acute stress reaction, you have to <u>notice</u> that you are in its grip and then perform <u>conscious</u> activities to escape from it. Any fully conscious activity will put the cerebral cortex back in charge of the emotional system and permit the full range of human emotions, not just anger and fear.
8. Examples of conscious activities that will break the stress reaction are;
   a. Consciously breathing (taking a deep breath requires consciousness)
   b. Consciously widening your vision
   c. Praying

d. Consciously relaxing your jaw and voluntary muscles.

e. Consciously seeking to discover and communicate with the source of the stress.

f. Consciously engaging in self-reflection, if the stressor is internal.

g. Consciously seeking assistance, when it is a problem you cannot solve by yourself.

h. Note: Exercising to metabolize the adrenal hormones released in the acute stress reaction will reduce the experience of stress. However, if the source of the stress is still present in your life, exercise alone will not solve the problem. You will still have to deal effectively with the source of the stress to rid yourself of it. If you don't, you will pass into the next phase of stress—chronic stress.

Dealing with chronic stress is the subject of the next three chapters.

PART II

THE CHRONIC STRESS REACTION

OVERVIEW

Chronic Stress: When Un-calm Persists

Not all human problems can be solved by communication. Nor do they necessarily evaporate with the passage of time. Many problems seem to go on forever, like death and taxes. Included in these perpetual problems are chronic illnesses and chronic pain, distrust between people and cultures, religious and political differences, and those relentless oppressors—time and money. Other sources of chronic stress are legal entanglements, being a victim of crime, false accusations and slander, and grudges.

Knowing how to deal with acute stresses can save you a lot of anxiety on a day-to-day basis. But when problems persist for more than a day or two, the strategy changes. This is because after about 24-48 hours the body shifts its automatic defense system from the hormone noradrenalin (fight or flight) to the hormone cortisol (endure). Our overview diagram now looks like this (See Figure 11):

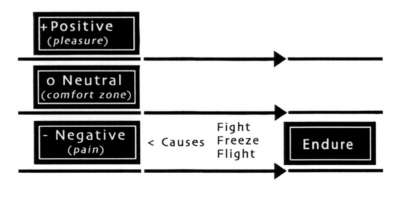

Figure 11

In the chronic stress reaction, the body and mind choose a different strategy. Rather than waste resources on continual fighting or running away, the body and mind now power down to conserve resources for the long haul. How to work with this system is our next topic.

CHAPTER 4

Endurance is Your Defense

Part one contains a surprising amount of new information for the average reader, unless you have already read quite a bit about stress. When I gave my weekly stress talks in Seattle, I used to permit a week to pass between discussing acute stress and chronic stress.

If you have the time and discipline, you might also like to let some time pass before starting this chapter, during which time you review what you now know about acute stress. Or you can just notice it as you continue to read. Notice how newspapers and television attempt to activate the acute stress reaction in you, and how charged words, half truths, and pre-formed conclusions are utilized for the sole purpose of activating the stress reaction. Remember, if someone can get you to activate the acute stress reaction (lose your cool), then they have got you functioning from a non-thinking part of your brain, and you are at a tremendous disadvantage.

Now onto chronic stress.

What is Chronic Stress?

You already have quite a few tools for dealing with acute stress. You know how to break the acute stress reaction (breathe, widen your vision, prepare to slow down, communicate with the source of the stress). In this section you will learn what to do if the problem cannot be solved in the acute stage and enters the stage of chronic stress.

Chronic stress is not as common in the animal world as it is in the human world. Presumably animals can quickly solve their territorial, dominance, mating, and food supply problems. Their battles are reasonably brief, accompanied by a lot of gesturing and posturing, sometimes breaking into fights, but for the most part coming to a permanent solution. As far as I am aware, animals do not hold grudges (elephants may be an exception), secretly harbor thoughts of revenge, retreat to re-organize an army in order to launch a new attack, pass on their hostilities from generation to generation, or embark on a campaign of disinformation in order to smear their opponents. But humans do. Churchill is famous for saying "Never, never, never give up!" It is good advice, and also why we can have chronic stress. We can never be certain that any agreement to end a human acute stress problem is really the end of it. There is always another day in which to fight.

In many instances, the situation is so much larger than the individual that it becomes impossible to resolve the acute stress situation. War, natural disasters, chronic illnesses, chronic pain, separations, kidnappings, legal entanglements, imprisonments, and difficult relationships can linger.

> **Example 1:** *Imagine this. You are a reporter in the Middle East, reporting on the Arab-Israeli conflict for an American news service. Recently there have been a number of kidnappings of Westerners by militant groups who do not seem to be under the control of any of the more recognizable power groups in the area. The reasons for the kidnappings are not clear, but they seem to be part of a loosely organized terrorist threat with uncertain goals.*

One day coming home from a tennis match with a friend, a car pulls up behind you and three men that you have never seen before pull you into the car. You are blindfolded and driven to a location you cannot identify mentally. You cannot contact anyone you know. You have simply disappeared. There is nothing that you possess to bargain for your freedom. Indeed, neither information nor money seems to be of any interest to your captors. Although you don't know it, it will be seven years before you are free again, but at this point you have no idea how long you will be held captive or even if you will be killed. To add to your mental anguish, your wife is pregnant with your first child.[1]

This, of course, is the true story experienced by Associated Press reporter Terry Anderson, a story he has recounted in the gripping *Den of Lions*. If you read his book, you will note that there are many moments of acute stress when the possibilities of violence or death suddenly loom. But the overwhelming terror is the endless claustrophobia and boredom of being locked in a small room for unknown amounts of time with other prisoners, with the virtual certainty that no one knows where you are and that nothing you can do[2] is likely to produce your freedom. At the same time you cannot predict when one of the guards will fly into a rage over some presumed challenge to their authority and unleash a violent attack.

Under conditions such as these, individuals soon discover the uselessness of fight or flight, although clearly there are times when moment-to-moment dangers again activate the acute stress reaction. For example, irritation at the prison guards; pain of wounds received at the hands of interrogators; disgust at the food or the lack of it; internal physical pains; moments of mindless fear when sudden, catastrophic imaginings flash through the sky of the mind; all of these may activate the acute stress reaction.

There is also the problem of staying alive for long periods of time under barely livable conditions. The body is stressed from malnutrition, poor sleep, inadequate physical exercise, and boredom—the colossal boredom. Endless periods of minimal physical and mental stimulation stretch out second by second, minute by minute, hour after

---

[1] Anderson, Terry, *Den of Lions*. Crown Publishers. Random House. 1993.
[2] Having no control over your future is itself an immense stressor. Gatchel, RJ, Bauma, A and Krantz, DS: *An Introduction to Health Psychology*. 2nd ed. New York. Newberry Award records. 1989

hour, for days, for months, for years.

For these long-term stressors, amazingly enough, the body/mind has a second emergency, survival technique, the chronic stress reaction, one of the most unusual and all encompassing reactions produced by our bodies. While the acute stress reaction is a volcano of sudden, explosive, decisive actions directed either towards or away from the source of stress, the chronic stress reaction is a prolonged, seemingly eternal, defense system—an impenetrable fortress against the ravages of unending stress—that keeps us alive in the midst of unbearable pressure. Its most extraordinary characteristic is that it works!

This remarkable system—the chronic stress reaction—appears to be capable of a lifetime of protection for the organism that has summoned it forth. There are, of course, costs to the organism that activates it, and sooner or later the chronic stress reaction will wear down its host, but for the chronic stress reaction itself, everything is sacrificed for the single goal of survival. If the catchwords for the acute stress reaction are fight, flight or freeze, the catchword for the chronic stress reaction is endure.

Behind the thickened walls of the chronic stress reaction lives the spirit of the trapped organism itself, maximally powered down for energy conservation, emotionally subdued for safety, guarding its very survival with layer upon layer of emotional and physical protection. Able to tolerate the tiniest of life spaces, goal directed towards endurance and survival, the spirit of the chronically stressed individual houses the hope that some day the siege it is experiencing will come to an end, and the life that it once lived will start again. Under the influence of will, often accompanied by prayer, this hope can become a conviction.

When neither fight, flight, nor communication with the source of the stress is capable of bringing an acute problem to completion, the body switches gears from the acute stress reaction to the chronic stress reaction. Internally, this is experienced as the switch from fight/flight/freeze to endure.

How Endurance is Achieved

How can the body/mind protect itself from the physical exhaustion of chronic imprisonment, the mental anguish of long periods of separation from one's family and loved ones, and the physical inactivity and lack of mental stimulation so often associated with chronic stress? How do people bear chronic illness, chronic pain, the need to provide continual care to a sick and dying relative, or to care for a badly injured child? How do people bear up under political repression, illegitimate authority, denial of basic needs and dignity, or prolonged medical or legal problems?

The answer is that our bodies, our minds, our will, and our spirit all have effective techniques for dealing with these terrible situations. Our bodies have a "power down" defense system controlled by the adrenal hormone cortisol, under whose influence we become physiologically subdued for long term survival. Simultaneously, our minds have the ability to create a meaningful story of the predicament in which we find ourselves, which can strengthen our resolve[3]. Our wills have the capacity to resist submission, seemingly forever, or to choose death rather than compromise. Our spirits have the ability to pray, to meditate, and to connect with God in terms that make sense to us. Long-term resistance to stress requires all of these. The body cannot do it alone.

---

[3] Few stories are as creative as that told in the award winning film, *Life is Beautiful.*

Endurance: Physically, Emotional, Mentally, and Spiritually

Chronic Stress: The Physical Defense

The hormone for the acute stress reaction is noradrenalin. It is released from the adrenal glands by an instantaneous signal from the brain (through the nervous system), whenever the thinking mind (the cortex) is overwhelmed. This initial burst of noradrenalin is accompanied by a slower but more prolonged release of a second adrenal hormone, cortisol. Cortisol is not activated by rapid nervous system connections the way noradrenalin is activated. Instead, it is released by a slower trigger, ACTH, a hormone that is released into the blood stream by the pituitary gland.

This means that even while the body is reacting instantaneously to deal with acute stress, it is simultaneously preparing itself to deal with chronic stress, should that become necessary.[4] Cortisol, the chemical mediator of the chronic stress reaction, is slower in onset and more prolonged in its effects than is noradrenalin. It fortifies the body for resistance to prolonged stress. Without it, the body would succumb.[5]

---

[4] It is now apparent that this initial discharge of ACTH also has the function of protecting the brain and body from too prolonged an effect by noradrenalin. That is, ACTH begins to put the brakes on the acute stress reaction at the same moment that the brain is activating it.

[5] Animals and humans who have had their adrenal glands removed cannot survive for long. In humans, the removal or destruction of the adrenal glands is called Addison's disease. It is characterized by the wasting away unto death of any person so afflicted. Because of the absence of the adrenal glands, these patients cannot defend themselves against stress or disease. Addison's disease is easily treated by supplying the needed adrenal hormones by pill or injection.

What are the effects of cortisol?

Oddly enough, we don't actually know how cortisol protects us during chronic stress, even though there is a vast body of information about this hormone. A recent textbook on the adrenal gland[6] points out "The association between the adrenal gland and stress is sufficiently well known to have entered popular mythology, and it is ironic that there is still no clear understanding of how corticosteroids protect against stress."[7][8]

Physicians have known for a long time that when patients are overwhelmed by the stress of a catastrophic illness, cortisol (also called hydrocortisone) can sometimes be life saving. It is known that cortisol causes the liver to break down the sugar that it stores, resulting in a rise in blood sugar. It is known that cortisol causes the retention of salt (specifically the sodium ion) from being lost in the urine, resulting in an increase in blood volume and therefore protecting against shock. It is known that cortisol protects against the sudden collapse of blood pressure when individuals are infected with bacteria that secrete a blood pressure lowering poison.[9] It reduces the severity of the allergic response when humans are exposed to an allergen, and it can be life saving in cases of extreme allergic reactions. So in various ways, cortisol strengthens and protects body systems.

On the other hand, cortisol has some seemingly unwanted effects in healthy individuals. For example, long exposure to cortisol causes loss of calcium from bone, resulting in osteoporosis and fractures. It can induce the development of cataracts, and it can decrease the resistance to infection including the reactivation

---

[6] Vinson, G.P., Whitehouse, B., and Hinson, J. *The Adrenal Cortex*. Prentice Hall, New Jersey. 1992
[7] Ibid. Page 181
[8] Fighting Stress with Stress Hormones. *Scientific American Mind*. Vol. 18 Number 2. P. 10. May, 2007.
[9] These bacteria secrete a toxin which opens blood vessels throughout the body resulting in a sudden and drastic drop in blood pressure.

of dormant tuberculosis. Under prolonged cortisol stimulation, ovulation may be delayed and sexuality is diminished; and blood levels of cholesterol, especially the "bad" cholesterol will rise.

So how do these effects explain the protective effect of cortisol on the physical body during chronic stress?

Although the actual mechanism may be discovered in the future, the best current guess is a hypothesis proposed by Munck, Guyre, and Holbrook in 1984[10], that what cortisol does is to protect the body from the overshoot of all the regulatory systems that go on hyperdrive during acute stress. In other words, cortisol protects the body by keeping things "cool" during the hyperdrive of acute stress.

Cortisol and Memory

Recently it has been confirmed that prolonged cortisol secretion shrinks a part of the brain known as the hippocampus, a structure in the brain's limbic system that is concerned with the storage of new memory associations. Under chronic stress, it is difficult to make new associations. As a result, learning decreases—a familiar experience for students stressed by learning.

Worry, however, is not an effect of chronic stress—but rather the result of the acute stress reaction being activated during chronic stress. Even under chronic stress, it is possible to experience acute stress, something that wears down the body even more quickly. That's why, even under chronic stress, it is best to stop the acute stress reaction and let the endurance reaction proceed on its own.

---

[10] Munck, A., Guyre, A.P., and Holbrok, N.J. 1984. Physiological functions of glucocorticoids in stress and their relation to pharmacological actions. *Endocrine Rev.* 5:25-44.

One casualty of chronic stress is a slight loss in the ability to learn new associations, especially if cortisol levels remain high. The next section describes how to combat this.

Chronic Stress: The Mental Defense

The story you tell yourself.

One of the most extraordinary studies on chronic stress is recounted by Peter Bourne, M.D. in his classic book, *Men, Stress and Viet Nam*[11]. Bourne measured urinary 17-hydroxycorticosteroids (17-OHCS) in 7 helicopter ambulance medics flying combat missions in Viet Nam. 17- hydroxycorticosteroids are breakdown products of cortisol that are excreted in the urine and that can be measured. They accurately reflect how much cortisol is circulating.

Unlike other men in combat, these helicopter medics had very low levels of 17-OHCS in their urine, which means their chronic stress was low despite the fact that they were exposed daily to extreme danger, including the possibility of capture, mutilating injury, or death.

What Bourne discovered about these men was that they "perceived their environment in a manner which was quite distinct from the way in which less intimately involved observers viewed it. ... Most of the men denied that that their job involved any real danger and readily named other units which they claimed had infinitely more hazardous duty [even though throughout Vietnam] it was generally accepted that these "dust-off crews" were exposed more consistently to high risk situations than almost any other outfit."

---

[11] Bourne, P.G. *Men, Stress, and Viet-Nam*. Little Brown and Company, Boston. 1970.

Bourne continues, "While minimizing the danger, they also tended to emphasize the rewards of the job in terms of the prestige they had among other troops ... as well as the frequent expressions of gratitude from the casualties they evacuated." What is interesting about these individuals is that their 17-OHCS levels were not only lower than the rest of the military population in Viet-Nam, they were lower than a comparable military population at Fort Dix in the United States. Even more extraordinary, their levels of stress hormones were lower than the general civilian population of the United States!

What was the explanation for their low cortisol levels (as measured by 17-OHCS in the urine)? Bourne first checked to be sure that the levels of adrenal hormones weren't low in these people because their adrenal glands were burnt out. In fact, these soldiers made very vigorous responses to minor infections, revealing that their adrenals were, in fact, very healthy. Their success at coping with their circumstances was due to other factors. They believed that what they were doing was important; they believed they were well trained to perform successfully; and they received praise both from the people they rescued and from their superiors in the form of medals. One individual was devoutly religious and "believed that God would protect him no matter how great the danger." Another individual did his job precisely the way he was instructed to do it, believing that if he did his job correctly, he would be immune from danger.

These soldiers reveal that in chronic stress, the story you tell yourself is a powerful determinant of how much stress you actually experience.

Optimism and Pessimism

Bourne's data fits nicely into the powerful observation made by Martin Seligman, PhD[12], that what we say to ourselves in moments of crisis is a powerful variable in determining the outcome of those situations. Working in the 1970's Seligman made an extraordinary observation that has changed the course of modern psychology—the discovery of "learned helplessness."

In the course of his research with animals, Seligman became aware that experimental animals could be rendered helpless when the conditioning experiments in which they were being shocked provided them with no avenue of escape. This experiment was fraught with both deep ethical and psychological implications.

The now famous experiment consisted of putting animals in a shuttle box. When they received a mild shock on one side of the box, they could jump to the other side. However, when they jumped to the other side of the box to escape the shock, they received a shock in the second box as well. They soon learned that "nothing worked." Instead of jumping, they just sat down on one side of the box, received the shock and did nothing at all except to curl up and whimper. Seligman called this reproducible response "learned helplessness."

This seemingly simple experiment has had profound implications in psychology, because it overthrew the prevailing opinion in psychology at that time that all learning was simply stimulus/response conditioning. B. F. Skinner had proposed the theory that all of animal and human behavior could be explained by the fact that rewarded behavior is likely to be repeated and that punished behavior is likely to be extinguished. We are nothing more than the results of our random conditioning.

---

[12] Seligman, Martin. *Learned Optimism*. Alfred A. Knopf, New York 1991.

Seligman showed that this was not the complete picture. Animals and humans are far more complex than simple reward/punishment systems. Animals and humans have an emotional life; they develop attitudes that are powerful influencers of behavior. These animals became helpless, not because they were being rewarded for staying still and experiencing the shock, but because they had realized that "nothing worked". If they were simply reward/punishment automatons, they would have continued to jump away from the shock until they became exhausted. But instead, they learned something emotional—the futility of all their efforts.

Seligman went through personal soul searching before deciding to reproduce this experiment. On the one hand, he realized he might have an explanation for the feelings of hopelessness that so many people experience. On the other hand, he was ethically concerned that he would be shocking animals who could not escape from the shocks he was creating. He determined beforehand that if he reproduced these experiments, he would not physically harm the animals, he would not do the experiment any longer than needed to make the scientific point, and he would then assist the animals in recovering completely from the experiment. It is to his credit that he succeeded in all these goals.

He then repeated the experiment with humans, only this time he used audible tones that individuals were asked to turn off. The experiment was rigged so that for some subjects "nothing worked." [At the end of the experiment, it was explained to the subjects that their failure was due to the experiment being rigged, so that no one was left frustrated by their inability to stop the tone.] The crucial aspect of the experiment was to understand what was going through the minds of the subjects at the height of their frustration and despair.

From many interviews, Seligman was able to piece together the mindset of people who gave up easily (whom he called pessimists) and those who tried harder and longer (whom he called optimists). What he discovered was that the crucial event in any crisis is what you say to yourself when the crisis hits, not what you say to yourself before or after the crisis[13].

Optimists, it turns out, explained their failure in three ways: 1) This failure is simply a one of a kind event. It does not mean that I will fail at similar events in the future. 2) My failure in this one instance does not mean that I am a failure in general. 3) There is probably something about this event that was outside of my control that caused the failure (and if I knew what it was and could have affected it, I would probably have succeeded).

Pessimists felt the opposite: 1) This failure is indicative of the fact that I always fail with this kind of problem. 2) In fact, it is indicative of the fact that I am a failure in general. 3) The fault undoubtedly lies with me (and I am probably incapable of correcting it).

Pessimists created self-talk that discouraged them and led them to give up quickly. Because of this discouraging self-talk, they were prone to depression. Optimists did not give up easily and were prone to confidence and faith.

To put it most simply, and a bit redundantly, pessimists were pessimistic and optimists were optimistic. But to say it that way misses the point that there is a choice in becoming optimistic or pessimistic. It is under our control. In terms of the language I use in this book, optimists broke the stress reaction by telling themselves concepts that kept them conscious and in control. They communicated with the source of the stress (their inner sense of self-worth) by stating that there was something odd about the situation, not themselves. On the other hand, pessimists told themselves

---

[13] This is why general experience with affirmations is that they are a nice idea, but they don't work when you need them.

that the problem was their inability to control any stressful situation. They gave up, thereby slipping into a slightly unconscious state, which then dissolved into the stress reaction and flight.

The story you tell yourself to explain chronic stress situations—and most importantly what you say at the crisis moment itself—has a powerful effect on how well you survive the stress. The most decisive variable is whether the story you tell yourself about the crisis is fundamentally optimistic or pessimistic. To quote Norman Vincent Peale, this is "The Power of Positive Thinking."

Will and Spirit: The ultimate defense against chronic stress

Even though science cannot as yet locate the human will and spirit within the human body, and even though we cannot precisely define these words, we nevertheless have a strong inner sense of what they mean. This is because we can see their effects in our lives and in the lives of others. We can understand what it must take for individuals to survive physical exhaustion and danger, to stand up against oppressive forces, to stand alone for what they believe in, or simply to survive meaningless, accidental tragedy. We speak about the power from within and the power from above, using will and spirit interchangeably in those situations. We understand the terms "will power", the "will" to survive and endure, the "will" to make a difference in the lives of others, and the "will" to give meaning to one's own life. Similarly, we say that we like a person's "spirit" when they show the ability to stand up to a challenge or to come back from adversity.

Even though we mean something slightly different by "spirit" and "will", they are clearly connected. By "spirit" we usually mean an internal life energy, generally arising below the level of consciousness, originating at the core of a person's being that by its very nature gives liveliness to the person. If an individual's spirit "soars", we know that their positive life energy is on the rise. If that spirit is "broken", we know that something crippling has happened to that individual's life force.

By "will", we generally mean a conscious effort, generated internally, of intense forcefulness, focused towards an end to which the individual is devoted. This can either be a resistance to an oppressive force or the creation of an internal force directed outwards. The greater the internal force, the stronger the will.

In general, then, by spirit we mean an energy that is unconscious in origin and spontaneously fills the person, whereas by will we mean a conscious focusing of this internal force towards a goal. The spirit seems to arise from God or Nature and is unfocused, while the will arises from the person and is an action of concentration and focus. The spirit is the source of the energy; the will is the lens that focuses and directs the energy.

People who are resistant to chronic stress seem to utilize both will and spirit. In general, we would say that their spirit energizes their will to survive as with Terry Anderson. Sometimes their spirit energizes their will to see a new social order (Nelson Mandela)[14] or to free a nation (Mohandas Ghandi). Sometimes the spirit energizes the will to make sense out of accidental tragedy (Joni Eareckson Tada)[15] or to find meaning in the presence of senseless evil (Viktor Frankl)[16].

Recently, there has been an outpouring of books and research articles on the role of faith and prayer in healing and in resistance to stress. These have been neatly summarized by Harold Koenig, M.D. in his book <u>The Healing Power of Faith</u>[17] and

---

[14] Mandela, Nelson. *Long Walk to Freedom*. Little Brown, and Company. 1994
[15] Eareckson, Joni. *Joni*. Zondervan. 1997.
[16] Frankl, Victor. *Man's Search for Meaning*. Beacon Press, Boston. 1963.
[17] Koenig, M.D., H.G. *The Healing Power of Faith*. Simon and Schuster 1999.

by Dale Matthews, M.D. in his book *The Faith Factor*[18]. According to one study done by Koenig, 90% of patients he studied with serious illness said they relied on faith to at least a moderate degree to help them cope, and 70% said they used religious coping to a major extent.[19] Numerous studies—summarized in both books—show that faith and prayer result in decreased depression and more rapid recovery from depression than for people who do not use religious faith to cope.

Among other benefits attributed to religious faith by Koenig are greater life satisfaction, less divorce, and higher rates of reconciliation when marriage problems do arise. These individuals also have healthier life styles, including less drug addiction and nicotine addiction, longer life, fewer disabilities, greater protection against heart disease and hypertension, superior immune function (probably from reduced stress), faster recovery from bereavement, and less total health care costs.

There are, of course, some negative effects from religious faith as well—primarily from fanatical adherence. These include withholding medical treatment when needed, rationalization for hatred against other groups, thought control (as in the Heaven's Gate and Jonestown mass suicides), and justification for being judgmental and insensitive to others[20].

What is interesting to me, is that when stress becomes serious enough to reach the life/death border, faith is the choice of humanity in at least 90% of the cases, as measured by Koenig. The reason for this is, of course, obvious. Only a transcendent being or spirit can bridge the gap from life to death, and since the treatment for acute stress is to communicate with someone who can do something about the problem, communication with God (as the individual understands God), is the natural choice.

---

[18] Matthews, Dale A. *The Faith Factor*. Penguin Books 1998.
[19] Op. cit. p.118.
[20] Joseph, Mary M.D. The Effect of Strong Religious Beliefs on Coping with Stress. *Stress Medicine* 14:219-224 (1998).

The topic of spirit brings to mind a famous medical anecdote. A patient had died with a rare disease. The family had given permission for an autopsy, and the body of the patient had been studied exhaustively by the new pathologist at the hospital. The pathologist presented his findings in great detail to the assembled physicians, going over each body system carefully and showing microscopic slides of the effects of the disease. At the end of the presentation, one of the clinical doctors remarked to the pathologist, "You have provided us with a superbly detailed description of the effects of this disease, but you haven't yet shown us why the patient died. Could you now tell us why he died?"

The pathologist answered, "If you can tell me what it was that kept him alive prior to his death, I am sure that I can show you what it was that was no longer present when I examined him."

Deeper than mind and body are spirit, the life within, and will power, our conscious ability to focus that energy. People who survive overwhelming stress use both to endure.

CHAPTER 5

Controlling the Chronic Stress Reaction

This chapter will give you an overview of how to cope with <u>all</u> the stressors in your life.

Although that may sound impossible, like all other complex problems, it is just a matter of handling them one step at a time. Many human problems cannot be solved, only managed. You cannot always force your enemies to be at peace with you, you cannot bring loved ones back from the dead, and some illnesses cannot be cured. But, based on the courageous examples of others, you can learn to cope with almost anything.

At the opposite end of the spectrum, I have treated many individuals who were not facing faith-defying catastrophes and yet were still overwhelmed. They simply had chronic, difficult problems that pushed them to the edge of their coping abilities. When they reached that point, daily acute stress problems were pushing them over the edge. They responded to these minor daily stress problems with extreme outbursts or withdrawals. Seemingly simple daily problems were unsolvable because they were being thrown into the same bin with an irreducible collection of unsolved, lifetime problems.

This reveals that what we usually mean by stress is the **<u>total burden of all the acute and chronic stresses of our lives at any given moment</u>**, not just the burden from the immediate problem. Whenever this total exceeds our ability to cope, we are not just stressed—we are overwhelmed. This chapter provides a tool for uncovering all the stresses of our lives and devising a strategy for dealing with them. As with any other problem control technique, the first step is to discover just how big the problem really is.

At first, it may be seem surprising that the total amount of stress we are experiencing in our lives at any given moment can be measured, but in fact it can be.

How Much Chronic Stress Have You Got?

Our knowledge about chronic stress comes from a variety of sources—from observing patients with chronic illnesses, from examining caregivers who provide day-to-day care for loved ones with relentless conditions such as Alzheimer's disease, from parents of children with cancer,[1] from soldiers while under battle conditions[2] and upon release from prisoner of war camps, and from astronauts in orbit. Anecdotal data comes from disasters of all sorts—from victims of starvation and natural disasters, from individuals who have been shipwrecked and floated for days alone at sea, and from explorers and their support parties who have become trapped by natural events. Data also comes from ordinary people who are evaluated for their chronic stress levels, using questionnaires and analyses of hormone levels in blood and urine.

Stress is measured by using two very different kinds of information:
1) Subjective information: This consists of self reported life discomfort obtained by questionnaire.
2) Objective information: This is the measured amount of stress hormones excreted by the body under stressful conditions into the blood and urine.

Surprisingly these two different measurements correlate reasonably well.

---

[1] Elmadjian, F. *Adrenocortical Function of Combat Infantrymen in Korea*. Quoted in op cit. #12, page 23.
[2] Bourne, Peter G. *Men Stress and Vietnam*. Little Brown and Company. 1970

Using the Holmes-Rahe Scale to Measure Your Stress

In 1967 Thomas H. Holmes, M.D. and Richard H. Rahe[3] made the seemingly innocent observation that the amount of social readjustment required by an individual to meet life's challenges correlated closely with their chance of becoming ill. Their crucial breakthrough consisted of demonstrating that it is the amount of accommodation an individual must make to life events that dictates how stressful that event will be for the person and is what we actually mean by the word "stress".

This inner perception of life accommodation matches very well with the objective amount of cortisol actually secreted by the adrenal glands in conditions of stress. Since cortisol is metabolized in the body to compounds called 17-hydroxycorticosteroids (17-OHCS) which are then excreted in the urine, measuring 17-OHCS in the urine provides an objective measurement of how much stress an individual is experiencing. The amount of stress subjectively perceived on the Holmes-Rahe scale by any individual correlates well with the amount of 17-OHCS secreted by that person into their urine.

Holmes' and Rahe's observation that it is the amount of life accommodation to an event that is perceived by us as stress may seem obvious. However, it is only obvious once it is clearly stated, and it was not at all obvious before they enunciated it. Most people think that stress is related to how serious the external event is, not realizing that it is the internal perception of that reality that results in stress. This observation has three important consequences:

1. The **first** consequence is far from obvious: The amount of stress an event causes in you is determined primarily by what the event **means** to you.

---

[3] Holmes, Thomas H. and Rahe, R.H. The Social Readjustment Scale. *Journal of Psychosomatic Research.* Vol.11 pp. 213-218. Pergamon Press. 1967

It doesn't matter whether the life event causing stress is a happy occasion or a sad occasion, a pleasant event or an unpleasant event, or even whether it is pleasurable or painful. What matters is <u>how much</u> life accommodation that event requires of you—how much the event pushes you out of your comfort zone.

Preparing for a wedding can be as stressful as dealing with a car wreck, if wedding preparations push you as far out of your comfort zone as the car wreck does. Reconciling with a spouse can be as stressful as breaking up with that spouse, depending on how much social adjustment is required. The crucial issue is not how pleasant or unpleasant the event is but how much social, biological, or psychological accommodation is involved—and therefore how much cortisol the adrenal glands have to manufacture and secrete to cope with the event.

> **Example 1:** *When I was in high school, I enjoyed how fellow classmates looked when they came to school wearing an arm cast, because they had fractured their arm in sports. I liked the attention they got when everyone signed their cast. The cast and sling made them stand out—even seem valorous, as though they were soldiers wounded in action. As crazy as it sounds, I was exhilarated when I finally broke my arm playing sports, because it added to my self-image. I had achieved my goal. The amount of accommodation I required was zero, because I had already rehearsed it in my mind so many times. On the other hand, breaking a string in my favorite tennis racket caused me significant stress, because I had decided that I only played really well with my best racquet. Having to play with a less favored racket, while my favorite one was being re-strung, required some accommodation and was therefore stressful.*

Clearly then, it is not the event itself that determines the stress, but what that event <u>means</u> to the individual to whom it has occurred. That meaningfulness is ultimately translated into how much adrenal hormone is secreted to handle the stress.

2. The **second** important outcome of Holmes and Rahe's work is that they were able to <u>quantify</u> just how stressful various life changes are. What they did was to administer a questionnaire to 394 individuals who were

at the time not going through any of the crises listed on the questionnaire. They assigned an arbitrary value of 500 life adjustment points to the accommodation that getting married would require. Then they asked each of their test subjects to rate whether the rest of the life events on the list would require more or less accommodation than marriage. To do so they asked the question, "Compared to marriage, would the readjustment take longer or shorter to accomplish?"

In this manner, Holmes and Rahe were able to construct a scale of life adaptations which, amazingly enough, has persisted to the present day as a useful measure of accommodation. Even though this scale is colloquially called the Holmes-Rahe stress scale, it is not a stress scale. <u>It is a measure of the amount of social readjustment (accommodation) that any life event requires</u>.

This is crucial to realize. Remember, what is hard on our health is not the external stress itself but the total social readjustment that the stressor requires of an individual—the amount of energy needed to accommodate to a life event. The reason that many of us do not accomplish as much in life as we would like to accomplish is not because we are stressed, but rather because we cannot handle the total accommodation that each life change requires.

3. The **third** important outcome of the Holmes-Rahe scale is that it reveals that it is not any one item in our lives that causes us to feel stressed, but rather the sum of all the stresses going on in our lives at any one time. This conclusion is extremely valuable, because it provides us with a strategy for managing the chronic stress in our lives.

The amount of stress that any of us feels on a daily basis is equal to the total amount of life accommodation we need to make to stay in our comfort zones.

This is experienced as the total amount of endurance we need to exert to stay comfortable, and this translates into the total amount of cortisol our adrenal glands need to secrete "to keep us keeping on."

How to Use the Holmes-Rahe Scale

The Holmes-Rahe scale explains why a lost contact lens under some circumstances can send us into explosive fury and under other circumstances it is hardly noticed; why some days we are screaming at everyone and everything, and on other days, catastrophes can befall us, and we remain calm. The crucial factor is how many other unresolved accommodations are going on simultaneously. If our Holmes-Rahe score is very high, a broken pencil point might just put us over. If it is very low—perhaps so low that we're bored—a catastrophe might be just what we're looking for to keep us busy and put us into our comfort zone!

Figures 12 and 13 explain this visually. In Figure 12 you will first note that any unresolved acute stress problem becomes a chronic stress problem. Acute stress problems that are resolved, of course, do not persist. As chronic stress problems accumulate, the Holmes-Rahe score increases and coping reserve diminishes. All unresolved acute stress problems become part of the chronic stress load.

Visual Summary Part I & II
Acute & Chronic Stress

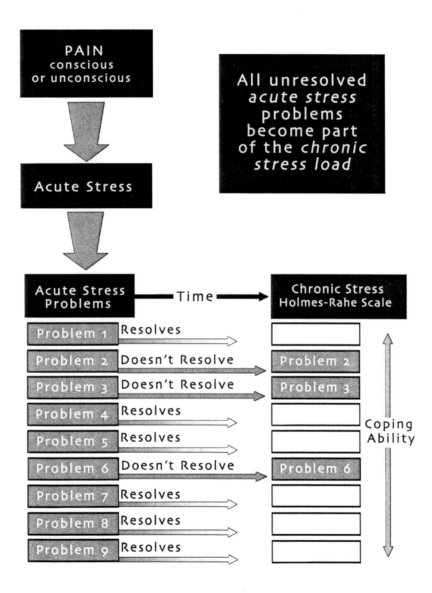

[Figure 12]

Figure 13 shows three common situations. The first (13.1) shows an individual who is reasonably comfortable. There are enough chronic problems to keep life from becoming boring, but not so many that the person is in constant stress. Figure 13.2 shows the situation where there are so many chronic problems that the individual has exceeded his coping ability. In this circumstance, *any* problem will provoke outbursts of anger or induce a collapse into overwhelm.

Figure 13.3 shows the situation where there are not enough problems in a person's life. This is the familiar problem of boredom. Boredom is a stressor and sooner or later will provoke the need to create a problem to return us to the comfort zone.

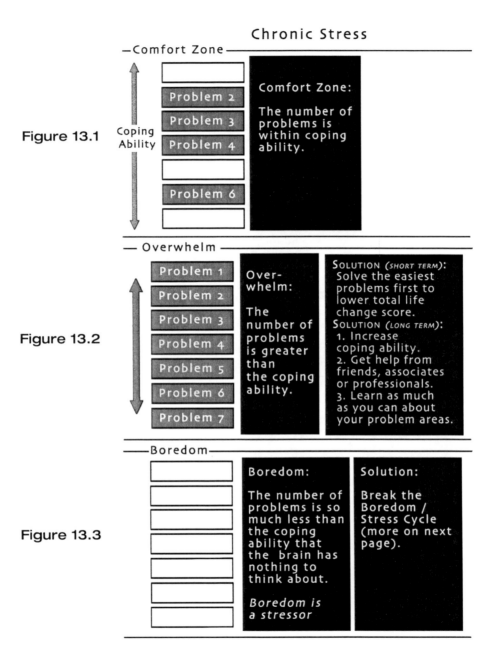

Figure 13.1

Figure 13.2

Figure 13.3

Chronic Stress

Comfort Zone

Coping Ability

Problem 2
Problem 3
Problem 4

Problem 6

Comfort Zone:

The number of problems is within coping ability.

Overwhelm

Problem 1
Problem 2
Problem 3
Problem 4
Problem 5
Problem 6
Problem 7

Over-whelm:

The number of problems is greater than the coping ability.

SOLUTION (SHORT TERM): Solve the easiest problems first to lower total life change score.
SOLUTION (LONG TERM):
1. Increase coping ability.
2. Get help from friends, associates or professionals.
3. Learn as much as you can about your problem areas.

Boredom

Boredom:

The number of problems is so much less than the coping ability that the brain has nothing to think about.

Boredom is a stressor

Solution:

Break the Boredom / Stress Cycle (more on next page).

Figure 13

EXERCISE: *Constructing Your Own Holmes-Rahe Scale*

I am now going to ask you to do some work. If you don't feel like doing it now, skim the exercise, read other parts of the book, and then come back to it. But if you are serious about controlling your stress, this will assist you. It is somewhat like balancing your checkbook. It takes work, but you need to balance your checkbook to gain control over your finances. This exercise is a stress checkbook.

First, you are going to add up all the stresses in your life. You can think of this as your outstanding debts. You are then going to figure out your coping ability. If your coping ability exceeds your stresses, you have "money in the bank." That is to say, you can still handle the need for more life accommodation without flying into acute stress.

If your stress level is very close to your coping ability, you can handle your stress, but any small life challenge is going to put you over into acute stress. If your stress level exceeds your coping ability, you probably don't need me to tell you that you are stressed on a daily basis; but I may be able to assist you in getting yourself back into the comfort zone.

We are now going to construct your own personal Holmes-Rahe scale. When we are finished, we are going to use it to estimate your coping ability. Use the grid below (which follows the instructions) to complete the exercise.

INSTRUCTIONS

1. In column 1, write down <u>all</u> the problems that are bothering you right now. This may take some time, and you may want to come back to it later and add problems as they occur to you. Some of these will be acute problems and some will be chronic. Put them all on the list. After you have written some down, you may think of more. Add them to the list. Don't worry about how long the list becomes, because it will self-correct over the next few days, as you work with it.

2. Assign 100 points to what you currently consider to be your <u>worst</u> problem.

3. Next assign points to <u>all</u> of the other problems on the list, based on how closely the problem approximates your worst problem. For example, if your worst problem is a child who won't have any contact with you, then assign that problem 100 points. If another problem is a need to increase your income, then assign that problem a score that reflects how much more or less you worry about that compared to the first problem.

Don't worry whether or not you are assigning the precisely correct value to each problem. As you continue to assign values to problems, they will sort themselves out into the proper values.

[If as you are assigning values to problems, you suddenly decide that there was a problem that is actually worse than what you originally thought was your worst problem, just assign it a number larger than 100. The goal is to get a handle on the totality of your stress.]

4. Continue to assign points to each of your other problems, using previously evaluated problems as benchmarks.

5. Look up and down the list to see if all the problems have been assigned approximately the right score compared to each other. If you stick with it, the work you put into the exercise will be rewarded at the end.

6. Add up all the points. (Be sure to put other problems on the list as they occur to you.)

7. This total number of points is a measurement of the total stress you are under right now. It is true that the number only has meaning for you, but it is going to be compared to your coping ability—not to that of other people.

8. We are now going to estimate your <u>coping</u> ability. There is no universally accepted scale for measuring coping, but as you will see, it is possible to estimate it on a person by person basis. Look at your total stress score.

At this score, are you relaxed and in your comfort zone? If so, add about 10 per cent to the score and use that as your temporary coping level score. If you are willing to work with this list for a few days or longer, check to see how much more life accommodation you can add to the list before you fly into acute stress. Sooner or later, you will have a day that sends you into acute stress. When that happens, return to the list, put the newly acquired problems on the list and assign them a score. The new total stress score will be a number that is <u>above</u> your coping ability. In this manner, you will be able to zero in on your current coping capacity. I am going to use this in the next chapter to assist you in getting out of stress and back into comfort, when needed. You will also find suggestions on how to enlarge your coping capacity as the book progresses.

OR

At this score are you flying off the handle? If so, then clearly this score is above your coping ability. As you begin to successfully handle some of the problems on your list—and the next chapter will assist you in doing this—you will sooner or later return to your comfort zone. When you notice that you have returned to comfort, subtract the problems from your list that have either been solved or disappeared, and your new stress score will be probably be your stress limit—and therefore your maximum coping ability.

OR

At this score, are you withdrawn and wanting to hide from life? If so, then this total is also beyond your coping ability. (Note: Since depression can either be a temporary condition caused by sudden stress or a medical condition requiring professional help, I would recommend checking with a medical professional first before assuming that a desire to withdraw is simply a reaction to chronic stress.)

10. Now that you have a total stress score and a first estimate of your coping ability, continue to update the list and figure out over time, the number of life accommodation points you can successfully cope with without becoming stressed and what the stress score is when you "lose it".

11. **Now here's what is truly valuable about this list. If you are stressed, solving *any* problem on the list will reduce your total score and move you closer to being out of stress and back into your comfort zone.**

12. In other words, you don't have to solve your worst problem or problems to cope. Any problem on the list that you can solve, no matter how small, will lower your total stress score and make you feel more comfortable.

13. Over time, you may notice that solving **any** small problem—such as fixing a clogged sink or changing a light bulb—may get you out of stress and back within your coping ability, even though you might think that solving your biggest problem is the only strategy that will work to make you unstressed.

14. Finally, you will discover that solving the easy problems on the list keeps the total stress score low enough so that you remain mentally clear to deal with the tougher ones. Remember, in stress, the thinking part of your brain doesn't work well. Getting back into your comfort zone frees your brain up to think and act consciously.

So, take a chance and start making a list of all your problems and their relative values. It will work to keep you out of stress.[4]

---

[4] If you simply cannot tolerate making lists, at least start this one before going on to the next chapter. Put down at least one or more of your worst chronic stress problems, assign them a number near 100, and then go on with the book.

PROBLEM #	PROBLEM DESCRIPTION	STRESS POINTS
1.		
2.		
3.		
4.		
5.		
6.		
7.		
8.		
9.		
10.		
11.		
12.		
13.		
14.		
15.		
16.		
17.		
18.		
19.		
20.		
21.		
22.		
23.		
24.		
25.		
26.		
27.		
28.		
29.		
30.		

TOTAL STRESS SCORE	

How Our Bodies Change from Stress to Relaxation

There is one final chronic stressor that needs comment, and that is boredom. Boredom is a chronic stressor with a different solution from all the other chronic stressors, because you cannot solve boredom by lowering the Holmes Rahe scale. Actually, you have to **raise** it (see Figure 14).

The Stress/Boredom Cycle
and How to Break it

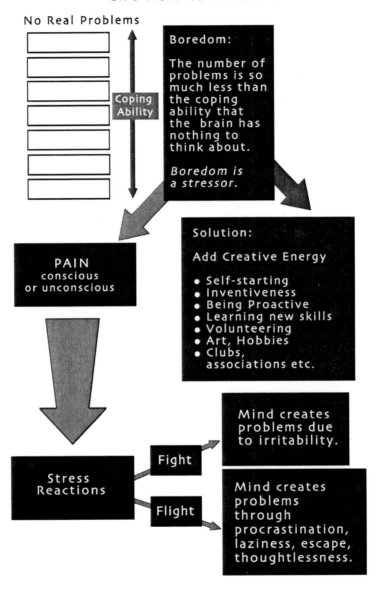

Figure 14

Boredom is a stressor (by definition a situation in which the cerebral cortex doesn't know what to do) in which the individual has so few problems that the central nervous system is in pain from inactivity. But since boredom is a stressor, it, too, will unconsciously activate a person into fight (irritability or arguing for the sake of arguing) or flight (sleep, mindless entertainment, perhaps drugs or alcohol). Asking the bored individual to discover the source of the stress is a fruitless activity, because there is no source of stress, just boredom.

Some people become enamored of the escape from boredom, either descending into drug or alcohol addiction or making a career out of sleeping and watching television. Other bored people are "looking for a fight." Since fight is more energetic than boredom, meaningless arguing or actual physical fighting can become entertaining for a while, and it is an improvement over boredom. But since the fight is usually not about anything real, it too becomes boring and unpleasant and the individual drifts back into boredom.

This cycle of stress and boredom can go on for a remarkably long time. Some individuals and families seem always to be bored or stressed, never relaxed, never engaged in life, never productive, never creative or inventive. Bored individuals are bored because they are unable or unwilling to connect to anything or anyone in their environment. They simply drift away from life and, when not bored, engage in meaningless fights.

The antidote to boredom—and to stress in general—is becoming involved in life. It is amazing how long the stress/boredom cycle can go on—especially in families and work situations—without anyone noticing it. The crucial piece of information needed to get out of it is for the person (or persons) trapped in it to break the stress reaction and to stimulate the thinking/communicating/creative part of the mind. This is what is meant by being pro-active.

When the cerebral cortex becomes connected to something or someone outside of itself, the mind passes from stress to non-stress. This is one of the reasons that music or other entertainments are so powerful. They require the cerebral cortex to be activated, and this in turn breaks the stress reaction. Curiosity, interest, participation, connection to people and events—all of these activities encourage the mind to flip from looking inside to looking outside. All of them will break the stress/boredom cycle.

This is why we need <u>some</u> unresolved problems to keep us interested in life, yet not so many that we overload our ability to handle them all. This is where the famous dictum arises that we need some stress to keep life from getting boring. Actually, as we have seen, this isn't true. What we need are problems that interest us, challenges with which we can connect, and obstacles that we enjoy. Stress arises when we have either so many challenges that we begin to withdraw from them or so few that we pass into boredom.

The Holmes-Rahe scale permits us to measure objectively whether we are bored, stressed, or comfortably stimulated.

EXERCISE

If you skipped over the personal Holmes-Rahe scale construction described in this chapter, at least start it before going on to the next chapter. Put down at least one or more of your worst chronic stress problems, assign them a number near 100, and then go on with the book. Once you have started, your mind will start handing you the other problems increasingly quickly, and you will be able to jot them down and assign them reasonable stress numbers rather easily. Before you know it, you will have quite a list. The constructed list will make the next few chapters much more interesting.

Note: I was not sure how long to make the practice list for the average reader. One of my patients had 110 problems, and believe it or not, over the ensuing 6 months we discussed them all. We discovered that some were duplicates of others, that others were interconnected, that some were symptoms of very simple physical problems easily handled by common medications, that some were truly difficult and required a lot of thought and commitment to new learning, and that there were still others that hadn't yet made it onto the list. But the result was that she changed her attitude from intense pessimism to intense optimism, and she moved from self loathing to self respect.

I had another patient who made the interesting observation that the list never goes to zero. I reminded her how fortunate that is. Zero is boredom.

CHAPTER 6

Coping With Chronic Stress

In the last chapter, I explained how to measure the amount of life accommodation you experience on a daily basis. Coping ability is the <u>total</u> amount of accommodation you can handle without falling into fight, flight, or panic. It would be helpful if we could also measure each person's coping ability, but it is not at all obvious how to do this.

Thankfully, no one is willing (or permitted) to conduct controlled experiments in which people are submitted to relentlessly negative conditions, just to figure out what produces superior coping! So we have to learn what we can from survivors of catastrophes and from people who have coped successfully with all known adversities.

People who achieve high life accommodation scores without getting stressed are better copers than those who become stressed with very low scores. Put most simply, coping reveals how much life change you can accommodate without spilling over into acute stress. If the slightest irritating remark by a family member or friend causes you to explode, you're very close to your chronic stress limit. If you can survive a major emotional blow without too much of a ruffle, you're well within your comfort zone on the chronic stress scale and have great coping ability.

One of the now famous uses to which Dr. Holmes put his Life Events scale was to predict who would be injured on the University of Washington football team during a certain football season. To do this, he administered the Life Events scale to the University of Washington football team at the beginning of one season and then predicted that the people with the highest scores would be the ones most likely to get hurt. His results were remarkably accurate.[1] It is important to realize that this experiment assumes that the coping skills of each of the members of the football team were about equal.

Some people have publicly demonstrated phenomenal coping skills. Clearly Viktor Frankl, Corrie ten Boom, and Elie Wiesel, all of whom survived concentration camp experiences; Terry Anderson, who survived a long political abduction; Nelson Mandela, and Mohandas Ghandi, who survived political imprisonments; John McCain and many others, who survived being prisoners of war; and Joni Eareckson Tada and Christopher Reeves, who bore accidental quadriplegia with grace, have world class coping ability. But so do thousands of other people whose names we have never heard, who survive day after day in difficult or impossible conditions, maintaining hope, faith, and cheerfulness.

If you read the literature on people in crisis, generally these individuals say that they were able to survive difficult and even life threatening circumstances because they:
   1) had faith in God[2],
   2) felt they had a mission to accomplish[3]
   3) felt they had something or someone other than themselves to live for[4]
   4) felt a responsibility to other people to keep going[5],
   5) had a strong social network of friends or associates who gave them strength or in whom they could confide,

[1] Personal communication from former University of Washington Professor of Psychiatry, Donald Dudley, M.D.
[2] Op cit. Koenig
[3] Op cit. Bourne
[4] Henry, J.P. and Stephens, P.M. *Stress Health, and the Social Environment*. Springer-Verlag. NY 1977. Chapter 11.
[5] Boukreev, Anatoli and DeWalt, G.W. *The Climb: Tragic Ambitions on Everest*. St. Martin's Press. 1997.

6) identified with a family, social group, or race which has a tradition of endurance, and

7) tended to approach life optimistically rather than pessimistically[6].

On the coping questionnaire in my office, we ask patients

1) if their parents or their role models were people who could cope well with adversity;

2) if they can express their feelings easily to other people or if they keep their feelings bottled up inside;

3) if they are optimistic or pessimistic about the future.[7]

4) if they feel that they can affect the outcome of their problems by their own actions or if they feel that they have no control over their fate[8], and

5) if they feel strong and healthy or are concerned that their own health problems will prevent them from facing difficult situations head-on.

All of these factors—which represent both external and internal strengths—are collectively called coping ability. To use the Holmes scale accurately, you need to assign yourself a score for coping ability, since with greater internal strength you can cope with greater outer challenges. This produces a more accurate measurement of an individual's ability to handle his or her chronic stress than simply measuring the life change. With more coping ability, you can handle a lot more stress.

This results in the stress/coping seesaw (see Figure 15). The greater the stress, the more coping strength you need to stay in balance and out of overwhelm. The lower your coping strength, the more you have to avoid stressful situations to stay within your comfort zone.

---

[6] OP cit. Seligman.

[7] Coping questionnaire. Washington Institute of Neurosciences. 1990.

[8] Faith in the efficacy of prayer would be considered internal locus of control, because the person praying is initiating the petition and utilizing his or her own faith.

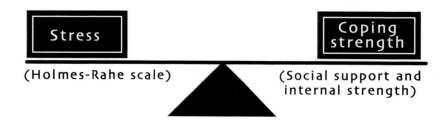

Figure 15

Because there is no agreed upon scale for measuring coping ability, I suggest that people discover their own Holmes-Rahe comfort zone. The exercise at the end of the last chapter does just that. As long as you are in your own comfort zone, regardless of the actual numerical stress score, you will be able to handle all the items in your life.

Once you exceed your comfort zone, you will need to take one of two actions:

    1) **Reduce** the Holmes-Rahe score back into your comfort zone by bringing some items on your list to completion or

    2) Find ways to **increase** your coping ability.

You can reduce your Holmes-Rahe life accommodation score

    a. by solving <u>any</u> problem on the list or

    b. by reducing the number of activities requiring your attention.

You can learn to increase your coping ability by

    c. Solving the simple problems first

    d. Finding the common cause of many problems

    e. Tackling the big problems by

        i. Developing an interest in them

        ii. Adding faith, courage, and persistence

        iii. Encouraging yourself with a support network of friends and family

        iv. Getting advice from experts

        v. Becoming a practical learner

        vi. Getting into good enough physical shape to have the energy you will need to succeed

        vii. Becoming creative and inventive

        viii. Staying ethical (so that you don't create new problems faster than you can solve the old ones)

Here's how to do it.

Reduce Your Total Stress

Solving the simple problems first.

It is hard to realize when you are overwhelmed that doing almost anything productive will reduce that feeling. Many people have discovered this strategy spontaneously. When overwhelmed, they may have learned by habit that organizing their work space, cleaning their house, putting everything away in proper folders or drawers, organizing papers or closets, all add a note of order to their surroundings and therefore to their thinking. Paying bills, responding to correspondence, making needed telephone calls, or simply making a list of everything to be done similarly organizes one's thinking.

The reason that simple organizing works to reduce overwhelming stress is that the body and mind work on a buffer system. What "buffer" means is that every organ in the body, whether it is the heart, lungs, kidney, liver, or mind, has an immense capacity to tolerate stress or abuse without symptoms appearing. Symptoms of disease usually do not appear until the organ is close to overwhelm. This is why doctors look for signs of early organ damage either through blood tests or through "function" tests—such as the treadmill exam for the heart—which push the organ to its limits. If doctors were to wait for symptoms to appear, they would not notice disease until it was already quite advanced.

The same is true of the mind. As the need for life accommodation increases, individuals are often not aware of it until they are nearly at the edge of their comfort zone. Coping is the mind's buffer system. As life accommodation increases, people find that they can cope successfully up to a point, when suddenly they cannot cope at all and need help. Usually they don't notice the increasing demands on their time and energy until they are close to the edge—then suddenly, they are overwhelmed. This is the explanation for the oft-heard phrase, "If one more person asks me to do something today, I am going to scream."

Fortunately the opposite is true as well. Just as small amounts of medication may reverse heart failure or hypertension, so small amounts of bringing any of life's problems to completion will restore coping capacity. A relentlessly upsetting divorce custody battle may have an individual at the edge of his or her coping ability, but sometimes just getting a few small things accomplished in a day restores the ability to think. The reason for this is that even the "small things" that need to be done add to the total life accommodation score. If a person is just over the upper limit of comfort, reducing the accommodation score by just a few points may restore coping ability, even though the total score remains high.

When you are at wit's end, taking almost any problem on your list to completion will reduce the Holmes-Rahe scale and will get you back within your coping ability.

Find the Common Causes

A second advantage of looking at a Holmes-Rahe scale is the discovery of common causes underlying many problems.

For example, if you are stressed around learning, every life situation that requires learning becomes added to the total chronic stress score, and you begin to avoid all situations that require new learning. If you are stressed around dealing with money, every interaction that requires you to charge someone for a service or ask someone for a fee creates stress. If you are stressed about your appearance, every situation in which your physical presentation is important will activate stress. You may already know this, but if you can see just how much of your total stress load is caused by the <u>same</u> underlying problem, you can begin to see how much more relaxed your life will become if you can learn to cope with the underlying problem successfully. Humans have learned to cope with every known problem through 1) faith and prayer, 2) learning, 3) ingenuity and creativity, 4) the support of friends, family, and associates, 4) expert advice, 5) hard work and constant practice and 6) the courage, endurance, and persistence to see their difficulty through to completion.

Looking at a complete Holmes-Rahe scale can help you identify the generic problems creating most of your chronic stressors. Identifying the underlying stressor may be difficult and may require assistance from others. This is because unconscious pain surrounds the underlying stressor, pain that is derived from early experiences with the problem. For example, if, when you were young, each time money was discussed in your household, there was arguing and irrational rage which frightened you, you may get a bit jumpy when the topic of money comes up later in life. It may then be hard for you to notice that a lot of your stressors arise from the fact that you don't like to talk about money or become intensely stressed whenever the topic comes up. The same is true for learning, personal appearance, or whatever causes you continual anxiety.

Since the critical topics of life (sickness, death, money, relationships, career, religious beliefs, political beliefs) are difficult for everyone, almost everyone goes into some sort of stress reaction (and therefore automatic behavior) when these topics are broached. If you were lucky enough to have a family that dealt non-stressfully with any of these, your ability to handle that part of life is dramatically improved.

> **Example 1:** *If you have ever removed snow and ice from your car following an ice storm, the following analogy will make sense to you. At first the total problem may seem overwhelming, but as you approach it, you notice that first you can brush the surface snow away rather easily. This is analogous to solving the simple problems on your stress list first. Next you get down to the ice. At first nothing can be removed, but as you chip away at it, sometimes you free up something like a windshield wiper blade that causes a large crack to form in part of the ice. Suddenly a large piece may fall off. This is analogous to finding the underlying cause of a large group of problems and dealing with all of them with the same solution. Once this happens, your confidence rises. Maybe cleaning off all the ice may not be that difficult. This is what happens when you solve one of the "biggies" of your life, like learning, appearance, relationship, or faith. It gives you great confidence that you can handle your other problems as well.*

To reduce the Holmes-Rahe score dramatically, you need to notice the common threads underlying many problems. A major thrust of life can then become learning how to deal with these underlying causes.

At this point, you need two skills: 1) the willingness to become <u>interested</u> in the problems that are your major stressors (rather than afraid of them), and 2) the ability to <u>learn</u> from people who already know how to deal with these problems. The result will be a dramatic increases in your coping ability.

Stress and Problem Solving

Become interested in the problem.

You can't make any progress on a chronic stressor if you remain frightened of it. Even if it is one of the topics in your life that you most want to avoid (for example, difficult relationships, personal appearance, chronic health problems, failures at learning, personal safety etc.), you have to confront it as a topic and become interested in it, if you are going to get anywhere in overcoming it. Interest activates the human cortex and shuts off the reptilian fear system from being in control. Interest leads to communication with people, books, internet information sources, support groups, and experts in the field. Interest generates the excitement of learning something new and turns a fearful problem into a tiny bit of pleasure, because growth is almost always pleasurable.

Activate faith, courage, and persistence.

Once you confront a problem, decide that you are going to become interested in it, and make one or two small steps towards learning about it, intense fear, embarrassment, and self-doubt will rapidly attack. This is because at this stage, it still requires conscious effort on your part to keep the reptilian fear system at bay.

What happens as you come out of a chronic stress reaction is that <u>the acute stress reaction is reactivated</u>.

This is truly important to understand. Remember that the reason the chronic stress reaction originally came to your rescue was because you were having an acute stress reaction that could not be resolved. Either there was no identifiable source of stress or else communication with the source of the stress was too frightening or simply impossible. So for your own protection, the body went into the chronic stress reaction, a type of long-term power reduction around the problem.

Now as you come out of chronic stress through confronting the problem and starting to interact with it, the original acute stress reaction will reactivate. You will once again experience the fight or flight reaction you originally felt when first confronted with this problem. You need a new solution to the fear or anger your originally experienced, a solution other than activating the chronic stress reaction. You need a <u>conscious</u> solution, not a reflex solution carried out by the body's protective mechanisms.

Finding a conscious solution takes <u>courage</u> to keep your cerebral cortex active, <u>faith</u> that you can eventually solve the problem, and <u>persistence</u> in the face of uncertainty.

Some people have been remarkable performers while facing chronic stress. Corrie ten Boom[9] and Viktor Frankl[10] stand out by having survived the concentration camps in World War II, while remaining ethical and sane. Corrie ten Boom is famous for her faith in God; Viktor Frankl is famous for finding a source of strength within himself. To get out of chronic stress, you will need either faith in Something or Someone

---

[9] Ten Boom. *The Hiding Place*. Bantam Books. 1974
[10] Frankl, Victor. *Man's Search for Meaning*. Beacon Press, Boston. 1963

bigger than yourself or great faith in your own abilities. But you will definitely need to activate faith, so that in moments of weakness when you feel like giving up, you have an inner or outer strength to call on for support.

Encourage yourself with a support network of friends and family.

Athletes and celebrities perform better when their fans are cheering. Children of families that emotionally support them do better than those whose families discourage them, although there are always exceptions. The problem for people in chronic stress is that the stress reaction itself makes you a loner, preventing people who actually want to help you from doing so. Stress is anti-communicative, so that even if someone is offering you a golden opportunity, it falls on deaf ears. The stressed individual doesn't even realize that he or she is actually pushing help away.

The non-stressed individual values friendships and alliances and makes continual efforts in both the social and work environments. This means keeping in touch with friends and family, with friends from school, with friends from professional and social clubs, from previous neighborhoods, and from day-to-day interactions.

Whereas it takes many years to build up friendships, it often takes only moments to lose them, often because of misunderstandings that lead to flares of temper, angry words, insults that cannot be forgotten, and breaks in communication. Most of these occur during moments of stress and are often words and actions that individuals wish they could take back.

Over many years I have suggested to everyone who heard my stress talks that they develop a new reflex with respect to relationships. Rather than "fight or flight", I suggest the reflex slogan, "fight/flight or communicate". The idea, of course, is that since "fight or flight" is itself a reflex—but one which seems to work better for animal societies than for human society—the way to improve it is to build upon what Nature has already installed. Adding the branch "communicate" to fight/flight accomplishes this by adding the uniquely human characteristic of sophisticated communication to Nature's built-in danger response.

As you live your life, try to remain on good terms with as many people as possible. You really never know when the person you took for granted in the past is the person whose expertise, support, or good will is what you need right now.

Get help from experts.

Most common human problems have already been handled successfully by someone. For many people, getting expert advice is humbling. Others are afraid to get it because of the embarrassment of admitting that there's something they don't know, the cost of expert advice, or the fear that it will make the problem worse.

There really isn't much to say about this except that if you're in trouble, and the solution is well known, get expert advice.

There are, of course, things to know about hiring experts. Checking credentials, getting recommendations from people you trust, clicking on a personal level with the person you hire, doing some fact-checking on your own, and insisting on getting your questions answered at the level you can understand them are all valuable traits in using experts.

It is expensive to use experts. You have to decide in the long run whether or not the advice is worth the fee. But if it is, pay the fee, and don't get stressed about it.

Learn how to learn.

There are two time-honored methods of increasing coping ability: relying on what you know yourself and asking for assistance from other people. Both learning (what you know) and relating to others (who you know) are properties of the human cerebral cortex. If an individual can stay conscious during chronic stress problems rather than succumbing to the stress reaction with its resultant unconsciousness, these two great skills of the cerebral cortex—the ability to learn and the ability to relate—become our foci. Most human problems are solved by what you know and by whom you know. Very few human problems are solved by going into the stress reaction.

The Ability to Learn (What you need to know)

The first great skill that becomes activated when one avoids the stress reaction and remains in constant communication with the situation at hand is the utilization of our natural ability to learn. For some people, however, learning itself is a stressor. When they are in a situation from which they could "learn themselves out", they become more stressed without really knowing why. The problem for them is that the word "learning" has come to mean something that happened at school, and which they convinced themselves they couldn't do.

I am aware that most people reading this book do not have problems with learning, although some may. From the point of view of stress and non-stress, however, learning means the process of gaining mastery over previously unknown material in order to solve the problems that <u>life</u> presents. This is quite different from school learning.

In order to transmit the huge body of knowledge that the human race has gathered from generation to generation, schools are forced to provide students with answers to many questions that they are not spontaneously asking. These answers are the solutions to problems that people once asked, but since we no longer live in the era in which the questions arose, it is very difficult to greet those answers with genuine curiosity and interest. As a result, learning can become equated with boredom, frustration, and anxiety. The lack of genuine curiosity about the information forces an individual to memorize it in order to retain it rather than soak it up through interest.

To overcome this, <u>the first step</u> for individuals who have anxiety around learning <u>is to re-awaken the natural questioning process</u>, the one that asked "Why?" at age four.[11] Lifelong learners have endless questions. People whose minds have retreated from learning have difficulty formulating the necessary questions about the situations they are in because their cerebral cortex finds itself outside its comfort zone. The acute stress reaction is therefore activated, the individual becomes thoughtlessly emotional, and dissolves quickly into fight/flight.

The remedy is to stay connected to the problem situation and allow the mind to crystallize the questions that spontaneously are occurring to it. Saying these questions aloud, writing them down, or asking them to someone else reinforces the process. An individual can know when he or she has reached an important question when the emotional mind kicks in with excitement, curiosity, and interest. The emotions are now in the service of thought and problem solving rather than in the service of stress.

<u>The second step is to edit, shape, and focus the questions themselves, so that they become more precise, using interest and excitement to guide the way.</u> The more exciting and interesting the question becomes, the more it is pointed at the problem within the stressful situation. When the question becomes focused clearly enough,

---

[11] Schacher, Roberta Kern. *An Experience with Intelligence*. Perisseia Publishing. 1998.

the mind will suddenly realize how to go about solving it—whether it is to gather information, to ask an expert, to go to a library (or other resource), or to perform an experiment[12]. When I worked in a research laboratory, the best scientists were the most excited ones. These were the people who asked the most sharply focused questions. Just hearing their questions activated the minds of listeners in such a way that it became intensely interesting to go about solving them.

The third and final step is to pursue the answer with great clarity. You know you have found the answer when you can apply it to the problem, and it works! Great clarity means that all the elements of the problem (the words, the symbols, the concepts, the techniques, the search, and the answer) are clearly understood.

If you can formulate a question that goes to the heart of a problem situation, can sharpen the question to the point that the method of solution appears, and follow through with the resources to bring that solution into reality, not only will stress disappear, but excitement, enthusiasm, pleasure, and joy will replace the problem. This is true regardless of the arena in which the problem arises and is the general experience with stress.

When stress disappears and clarity arrives, joy is the result. The answer is always larger than the problem.

Learning solves problems by tossing them around mentally until an item of interest appears, which the mind can grab. When the mind connects to the problem, the flow of energy is experienced as excitement. Excitement then leads to the heart of the

---

[12] The process is similar to that of Zen archery in which the archer holds the bow in relaxed tension until suddenly the arrow releases itself and hits the target. (See Herrigel, Eugen, *Zen and the Art of Archery*. Vintage Books. 1981) In this case, the question is the arrow and the answer is the target. If the question is honed precisely and held in the mind correctly, it suddenly will fly towards the answer hidden in the problem.

problem, at which point it spontaneously unravels producing a solution. (On really hard problems, each solution leads to bigger and more interesting problems.)

Only the unstressed mind can solve problems, because the stressed mind takes too narrow a view of the problem, thereby missing crucial clues. It cannot assimilate pertinent information, which is outside the problem (yet is crucial to its solution), and it is far too impatient to hone its questions in order to reach into the heart of the problem. Since the solution is always larger than the problem, only the unstressed mind can widen enough to see it.

Get into good enough physical shape to survive solving your problems.

As you begin to tackle your chronic stress problems, will you be able to physically endure the demands that will be made upon you? When you were in chronic stress, the chronic stress reaction itself powered you down. Now that you are coming out of it, you have to power yourself up.

Most stress books discuss the importance of the three major components of stress management—diet, exercise, and attitude. I focus a lot on attitude, because that is the point of view from which I see the world. But diet and exercise, the physical components of stress management are important once you decide to do something about your situation. Ken Cooper, M.D. has made a powerful case for the benefits of diet and exercise combined with stress reduction in his best selling books[13], as have numerous other authors. But it is also obvious. If you are going to turn the power down system off, you'll have to turn the power up system on. Here are the direct physical benefits to exercising:

---

[13] Cooper, Ken. *The Aerobics Program for total Well Being.* Bantam, Doubleday, Dell. 1985.

Exercise increases coping :

1. by using up the circulating acute stress hormones that are driving you into stress.

2. by building up your physical capacity for endurance rather than relying on cortisol to power it down.

3. by moving energy from deep inside the body to the surface (the skin becomes warm through increased blood flow). This increases physical contact with the environment.

4. by moving the mind from inward rumination to outward communication.

5. by releasing endorphins, which are neurotransmitters of pleasurable sensations. Pleasure enhances coping.

When you come to the point that you are seriously committed to reducing your stress, start exercising!

Become creative and inventive.

If you pursue your chronic stress problems using the strategies listed above, you will occasionally encounter a problem that no one in history has ever solved. For example, at the present time, we cannot reliably cure chronic pain, cure most severe mental and genetic illnesses, create wealth when needed, or make peace with people who insist on fighting. When I was a young research scientist, these were the kind of problems we tried to find! The chance of solving a problem that no one had ever solved had the dream of Nobel Prizes dangling in front of our eyes.

I agree that it is a lot less stressful trying to solve a previously unsolved problem in a research lab than dealing with the same unsolved problem in your own life. Nevertheless, there is a lesson to be learned here. In the case of the laboratory researcher, there is intense excitement. In the case of the individual, there can be profound depression. But the way out can be the same technique—research the problem, be inventive, and be creative.

To be **inventive**, you need a few key ingredients—the problem that your mind or life has given you, an internal discipline to stay conscious and positive so as not to succumb to the stress reaction, the ability to widen your vision so that you can make novel associations, a spirit that is strong enough to move forward despite failure, and a social milieu that gives you enough life support to have the time to experiment and reflect on the results.

There are loads of examples of people who have done just this. Candy Lightner and a group of women in California finally became fed up with no one solving the repeat-offender drunk driving problem and formed MADD[14], which tackled the problem head-on. The Odone family decided to research their son's neurological illness and discovered a treatment that seemed to offer some hope (Lorenzo's oil).

Historically, there are some wonderful examples of individual inventiveness and creativity. In 1855, using completely new methods of epidemiology, John Snow, M.D. ended an intense outbreak of cholera in London by removing the handle of the Broad Street water pump[15]. He carefully recorded every case of cholera in London, realized that they became more concentrated as one came closer and closer to the Broad Street water pump, pulled the handle off the pump, and the epidemic disappeared.

The life of Louis Pasteur is truly inspirational for anyone who needs convincing that the seemingly impossible can be achieved by creative thinking. As a young scientist,

---

[14] Mothers Against Drunk Driving MADD National Office 511 E. John Carpenter Frwy. Suite 700 Irving, TX 75062.

[15] Snow, John M.D. *On the Mode of Communication of Cholera.* London: John Churchill. New Burlington Street. England. 1855

Pasteur solved a problem in chemistry that had eluded experts. He discovered why seemingly identical batches of an acid called tartaric acid, obtained from grapes, sometimes caused polarized light to rotate to the left (when viewed through a special instrument) and at other times caused it to rotate to the right[16]. Peering intently at the crystals of this acid under the microscope, Pasteur suddenly realized that he was seeing two groups of crystals, not one. Though chemically identical, the crystals were mirror images of each other. By hand, he separated these microscopic crystals into two batches and placed them in his polarimeter. He discovered that one batch rotated polarized light to the left, the other rotated it to the right, thereby explaining the mystery. Inadvertently, he launched the field of stereochemistry, a fundamental discipline of biochemistry, which grows in importance every year. His solution was bigger than the problem.

What is crucial is the fact that he pursued the problem at the point of confusion as to why different batches of tartaric acid affected light differently, employing careful observation until he reached the point of clarity. This is how creativity solves stress. It searches for the confusion or lack of knowledge, honing in more and more precisely on the puzzle, until at the moment that the source of confusion is reached, vision widens and the answer explodes into a larger sphere of knowledge.

It is the lucky student, indeed, who somewhere in his or her education runs into a teacher who encourages the activation of natural questioning, the precise shaping and focusing of those questions, and the patient expectation that careful observation will ignite creative recognition from within. Curiosity is a muscle, inventiveness is a skill of visualization and association, and creativity is a discipline that needs to be practiced to mature.

---

[16] Dubos Renée. *Pasteur and Modern Science*. Anchor books. Doubleday and Co. 1960

Creative and inventive people respond to chronic stress by wondering how they will solve the problem, not how they will succumb to it.

Stay ethical!

Under pressure, there is an immense opportunity to cut corners, to drop your ethics, or to break the rules. If you cannot survive by playing within the rules, there is always the temptation that maybe cheating or creating a new set of rules will make life easier. This is a nearly universal temptation. It is the rare person who refuses to be goaded into breaking the rules, who triumphs ethically under duress, especially as the tension rises. I think that until each of us is tested, we never know what we will finally do under maximum pressure. Most of us probably hope that we will not be tested to the limit.

The problem, of course, is that every time you break an ethical boundary you add to the stress of the situation and create a bigger problem for yourself later on. Sooner or later there is the need for the cover-up, the denials when confronted, and the intense embarrassment when the truth is finally revealed.

People who maintain their ethics under intensely negative conditions become justifiably famous, either as martyrs, heroes, or leaders. Instinctively, each of us knows that in their circumstances, we might not have done as well. Life is often long, history is even longer, and eternity is longer still. Sometimes short-term pain is the smaller price to pay than long-term chagrin.

EXERCISE

Even though it is work, go back to the exercise in the previous chapter and decide to identify and confront one of your major, chronic stress problems. Get started on it, utilizing the suggestions in this chapter. Confidence follows achievement. If you succeed in resolving even one of your chronic stress problems, your stress load will drop immensely, and you will be a renewed person.

CHAPTER 7

Not Being Stressed by Stress
Staying Connected to the Problem

Connect with the Stressor

Daredevils are people who are not in any danger at all but who choose to place themselves deliberately in situations as dangerous as possible in order to feel alive. This includes people who engage in extreme sports such as race car driving, extreme skiing, jumping off cliffs with parachutes, jumping out of planes on surfboards, engaging in the most dangerous types of rock and mountain climbing, or jumping across impossible distances on motorcycles. Why do these people do it?

Interestingly, the reason these people deliberately increase their stress has a lot to teach us about handling our own stress. They are doing it not to avoid life, as the stressed individual might do, but to connect to life more strongly, as a person emerging from stress must do.

Recall from Part 1 that in the stress reaction, thinking is reflexly reduced, and the body is plunged <u>unconsciously</u> by noradrenalin into a fight/flight/freeze program by the limbic (emotional) and reptilian (survival) brains. Daredevils are activating this same system but by a completely different method. They are doing it <u>consciously</u>, not <u>unconsciously</u>. Their thinking brain (the cerebral cortex) is **on**, not **off**. They are functioning from their human brain, not their reptilian brain. They are in communication with their situation. They are not activating fight/flight/freeze reflexly, as do people who disconnect from the situation. They are activating noradrenalin consciously. As a result, the noradrenalin is heightening cortical pleasure, not limbic pain. These individuals are not running from their environment or attempting to destroy it. **<u>They are trying to connect to it</u>**.

This observation reveals the secret of superior coping. When you separate from the events of your life under the reflex activity of the reptilian brain, you see the events as stressors and you link noradrenalin to pain. When you connect to the events of your life, you see them as difficulties, opportunities, or simply the current issues you need to confront.

An easy setting in which to practice this is anytime you are in front of an audience or are called upon to speak in front of your peers. Instead of seeing your audience as separate from you and seeing yourself as isolated from them (the experience of stage fright), imagine that you are connected energetically to each person. Just by letting your eyes sweep across each face in the room, you will experience a momentary connection that will break the stress reaction[1]. Take a moment to connect to people energetically before you speak and the stress reaction will not form.

Once you are connected consciously to other people or to your own life adventure, the noradrenalin you activate will stimulate pleasure rather than pain. You will be in communication with your environment. You will feel as though you are being emotionally supported by a network of people who are rooting for you. These connections, both to the event and to other people, are experienced consciously (human cortex) and produce pleasurable emotions rather than pain and stress.

---

[1] I first read this technique from Thomas F. Crum in his wonderful book, *The Magic of Conflict*. Simon and Schuster, Inc. New York, N.Y. 1987.

Anticipate the Stress within Life

This concept of connecting to a problem rather than separating from it—which we can observe in daredevils—also explains how people who are in terrifying circumstances can survive as well. The most successful copers <u>connect</u> themselves to the event:

    i.   because their world view is wide enough to see the problem as something that could happen to a human being

    ii. because they see themselves as capable of dealing with the situation

    iii. because they have faith that God or karma is bigger than the specific situation

Put Faith in Yourself

For an event to be stressful, it has to be perceived as threatening or interminably boring. The narrower your comfort zone, the greater the diversity of events that you will find stressful. The wider your comfort zone and the more you can tolerate, the less you will find stressful. To be reasonably stress free, you have to be able to tolerate an immense variety of unusual and threatening situations, and you must also have a mechanism for tolerating long periods of boredom.

<u>If an event—no matter how dangerous—is not perceived as threatening, the stress system will not be activated</u>. One of the best examples of this is found in the *New Testament*[2] when the Apostle Paul and his companion Silas are preaching the Gospel in Phillipi. Because of a complaint filed against them that they were teaching citizens of Phillipi unlawful customs, they were beaten and jailed. Yet, because they did not find this treatment to be outside of their expectations as preachers of a new religion,

---

[2] *New Testament*. Acts of the Apostles. Chapter 16. verses 12-40.

they responded not with fight/flight/freeze but rather with the singing of psalms, all the while jailed and in chains. The event was not outside their comfort zone. The end of the story is well known. Following an unexpected earthquake, which loosed their bonds, the tables turned, and Paul and Silas found themselves offering stress reduction to their former jailer, a frightened individual who was now outside of <u>his</u> comfort zone.

Paul and Silas did not perceive the situation as stressful, because their perception of the event was that it was the normal state of affairs—perhaps even a highly desirable state of affairs—for them to be persecuted.

Perceiving yourself as capable of dealing with the situation

Viktor Frankl[3] has become famous for realizing during his Nazi concentration camp interment that no matter how much he was controlled, his inner <u>reaction</u> to how he was being treated could not be controlled. In other words, he truly discovered and experienced his free will while under maximum stress, and this one discovery energized him throughout the remainder of his life and became a source of inspiration and hope to many.

Use Your Faith in God

Eastern disciplines, such as Zen training, martial arts training, yoga, and meditation, have as their goal that <u>no situation</u> will ever activate the unconscious stress reaction, because nothing is outside your comfort zone. Everything can be faced; everything can be dealt with consciously. Christianity has the same goal. Since "all things work

---

[3] Frankl, Viktor. *Man's Search for Meaning*. Beacon Press, Boston. 1963.

together for good for those who are in Christ[4]" and since "nothing can separate you from the love of Christ[5]", the awakened Christian should be able to live a stress free existence. In fact, all religious systems have the same goal that neither death, capture, physical pain, nor separation from anyone or anything can produce stress. The reason is that on the inside the individual is permanently connected to Something or Someone who is eternal, powerful, beneficial, and unchanging. Presumably, God is not stressed, and there is no stress in Heaven. To the extent that you can connect to this, you can cope with anything.

I once read the story of a Japanese/American man who was interred in the United States during World War II. He was a devout Buddhist and felt that everything that happened to him was a result of his karma[6]. Without commenting on the right or wrong of his predicament, I noted that he was remarkably free of stress during his interment, because he accepted it as something normal within his world-view. He felt that he was paying back his karma from a previous lifetime and that in a way he was in a good situation, because now he had less karma to deal with in the future.

A strong connection to Something or Someone bigger than yourself seems to be essential for making sense of a situation during overwhelming stress.

What happens if you can't make sense of the situation, don't have faith in yourself, and don't have faith in Someone or Something bigger than yourself?

There are people whose entire world shatters; who lose everything and everyone that kept them alive, and are so horrified by events that they begin to separate from life. (I discuss this in more detail in the appendix, where I discuss post-traumatic stress disorder.)

---

[4] *The New Testament.* Romans 8:38

[5] *The New Testament.* Romans 8:39

[6] An Eastern belief that events in one's present life are the result of actions taken in the past (including past lives).

Needless to say, this is a desperate situation. But it is salvageable.

1. **Trust the hormone of the chronic stress reaction (cortisol) to protect you.**

The body can survive under amazingly negative conditions as I discussed in Chapter 4.

2. **Be open to assistance when it is offered.**

One of the oddest consequences of chronic stress is the inability to accept assistance when it is offered. This is a consequence of the fact that the chronic stress reaction arose originally as protection from an unsolved acute stress reaction. Therefore, if you are in chronic stress and someone offers you assistance, your instinctual reaction will be to be frightened because your mind will fear that it has to re-experience the original acute stress. However, you may be surprised to discover that when you stop fighting off communications, solutions to really difficult problems can sometimes find you.

3. **Make sense of the situation if you can.**

4. **Pay attention to your spirit.** In the darkest of moments, people in all circumstances, in all centuries, have discovered that it is not their thinking mind that is keeping them alive, but their spirit. Once that is encountered, a very different world—the opposites of stress—begins to flower. It is to this world that we now turn our attention.

PART III

THE OPPOSITES OF STRESS

OVERVIEW

Calm: the Opposite of Stress

As we saw in Part I, the essence of un-calm is the sense of separation that the stressed individual feels from both the situation and the people surrounding him. Stressed individuals feel alone and isolated, which is a central cause of their anxiety. Often they feel that no one can help them, possibly that no one cares about them. They are disconnected from their environment and from the people who inhabit it. They are threatened by events and therefore need to destroy those events or to escape from them.

Every tool used by stressed individuals is used to dominate or to escape. They seem remarkably unaware and unappreciative of attempts by their friends and allies to assist them. They become seemingly incapable of taking in new information or updating their old information as the situation changes. They exhibit a surprising lack of intelligence in decision making.

The opposite of stress is relaxation, connection and communication—the characteristics of the calm state of mind. If an acutely stressed individual can accept advice or comfort, she is well on her way to coming out of stress. Connection defeats stress.

If an individual can activate inventiveness or creativity, she will have succeeded in burying the stress reaction, because she is now connected to her problem. The calm individual is in communication with her surroundings, energized by her problem, extremely interested in the advice of friends and associates, appreciative of expert input, and clear on the reasons for her decisions.

The calm individual has a wider range of choices than attack or escape. If fighting needs to occur, it is done to reach a goal, not simply to defeat an opponent. This permits calm individuals to discover solutions that are "outside the box", because as their vision widens, more possibilities come into view. Particularly beautiful solutions to stressful problems are much bigger than the problem that called them forth, because the individual problem that initiated the creative search is merely a specific example of a whole family of problems in need of solution.

In stress, the reptilian brain is in charge, directing the emotional mammalian brain. In non-stress, it is the human cortex which is in charge, the part of the brain which communicates, visualizes, and looks for connections.

CHAPTER 8

DEVELOPING CALM

Finding Faith

The deepest connection one can make from oneself is faith in God. For some people, this is a looking outward. For others it is a looking inward. But in either case, it is a looking beyond oneself to Something or Someone larger than oneself. For Westerners this is a connection to a transcendent God. For Easterners, this is a connection to a transcendent Self. In either case, it is a connection that defeats the isolation of stress and instills the belief that assistance—in its most powerful form—is on the way.

Faith—that is, religious faith—is a certainty about communication along a channel that cannot be sensed but is believed in without doubt. When I was a Zen student, my teachers talked about the "doubt mass"—that collection of uncertainties that separates you from being totally committed to whatever it is you have faith in. When the doubt mass goes to zero, you are in communication with the object of your faith, and you do not feel alone. If you have faith in God, you do so because you believe that there is a benevolent intelligence behind the Universe.[1] For people of faith, stress strengthens their beliefs, and their beliefs in turn relieve them of stress. They are not alone.

Faith is very relaxing. When I was a child, I loved to watch Western movies and half-hour TV dramas. What I liked about the Western hero, especially the ones whose programs were on weekly, was that you could absolutely count on them. No matter how desperate the situation became for the townspeople or the new settlers,

---

[1] I have written of my own faith in *Jewish Doctors Meet the Great Physician*, edited by Ruth Rosen. Purple Pomegranate Productions, San Francisco, California. 1997. pp 55-68.

no matter how many outlaw gang members were arrayed against them, you could absolutely bank on their ability to save the day. Movies have been spinning this theme ever since, and they would be foolish to ever abandon it. The hero who never loses becomes an object of faith, even if they are fictional. Faith relaxes.

Some time ago, I came across a suggestion by Norman Vincent Peale that I alluded to briefly at the end of the last chapter. Although his suggestion struck me as simplistic when I first read it, I decided to try it and was surprised to discover that for me it worked. He suggested that just before bed, each of us should write down all the problems that are weighing on our minds, breaking down complicated problems into all of their parts, if we can. He then suggested that we give all those problems to God, go to sleep, and let Him deal with them. If any of these problems then crosses our minds as we begin to relax (which they probably will) just announce to them that they'll have to look elsewhere because they have been given to God for the night, and we'll pick them up again in the morning.

The technique is clearly an example of nighttime prayer, and I decided to give it a try. After about 6 months of doing so, I looked back at what I had written my problems were just before bed. I couldn't even remember what most of the problems were about, even though according to my notes some of them had been torturing me before sleep! Remarkably, most of them had just disappeared.

At the other end of the spectrum are another group of people who also have immense faith—not so much in God—but in themselves. Thomas Stanley, Ph.D. states that 94% of the millionaires he studied listed faith in themselves as their main action or thought process for reducing fears and worries.[2] Norman Vincent Peale himself begins his classic <u>Power of Positive Thinking</u> by urging readers to believe in themselves[3].

[2] Stanley, Ph.D., T.J. *The Millionaire Mind*. Andrews McNeel Publishing. 2000. Table on page 137.
[3] Peale, Norman Vincent. *The Power of Positive Thinking*. Prentice-Hall, Inc. 1952. page 1

To me, faith in God and faith in oneself are both important, and there really is no contradiction. If you believe in God, then you believe that you are "fearfully and wonderfully made[4]" and the possessor of a "sound mind[5]." In fact, the more you have faith in God, the more you can believe that what wells up inside you can be trusted. Similarly, the more that you practice your skills, the more you can rely on them when they are needed.

All of this is usually quite hypothetical, however, until the chips are down. We never know what we are made of until we are tested to the limits, a test most of us would just as soon avoid. Because of my interest in stress, I have made it a practice to read as many first person accounts of people in extreme conditions as I can.

I don't think I've ever read an account of someone surviving an overwhelming ordeal—although undoubtedly there must be some—who did not mention faith as one of the reasons for their survival.

The well known theologian, Paul Tillich[6], made this point when he asked people what they will do when the "foundation of everything" collapses, a situation which people encounter in war, natural disasters, plagues, illnesses, economic collapses, and betrayals. I recommend beginning the defense against stress by becoming very clear on exactly whom or what you will have faith in when the foundation of everything collapses.

---

[4] *The Holy Bible.* Psalm 139:14
[5] *The Holy Bible.* 2 Timothy. 1:7
[6] Tillich, Paul. *The Shaking of the Foundations.*

Activating Prayer

Prayer is probably the most widely used antidote to stress throughout the world, at least among people who use it rather than drugs or alcohol to confront psychological pain. Clearly, drugs and alcohol take the experience of stress away from the sufferer by being anesthetic substances. But they are famous for ultimately not working. They tend more to destroy the person experiencing the stress rather than dealing with the stressors themselves.

Prayer, on the other hand, satisfies all the requirements of the perfect stress reliever. First of all, it is conscious, and thereby breaks the stress reaction. Secondly, it slows you down by requiring you to enunciate what the problem really is. Third, it forces you to widen your vision to the extreme, to the greatest width that can be imagined, because in asking God for help you are acknowledging the presence of Someone or Something larger than the Universe itself. Fourth, you are asking Someone or Something for assistance, who by definition has the capacity to discover the source of the stress and to do something about it. And finally, since prayer is a communication, you activate the very antithesis of stress, which is communication and connection.

Faith and prayer create a foundation of courage that permit an individual to face any challenge with confidence. Because they add the idea of eternity to our lives, they loosen the grip of fear we feel because our lives are finite and because all of us must face death. Challenging this deepest of fears—that everything must be accomplished before we die—has the effect of softening the stranglehold that time has on our lives. Unbeknownst to us, in the deep background, the fear that there is not enough time creates in us a perpetual "hurry sickness." In the deep background we are impatient and as a result have the sense that something is always wrong. Being aware of an eternal view weakens this continual sense of impatience, turns off the "hurry-up hormone" noradrenalin, and reveals that most mysterious of virtues, patience.

Eliminating "Hurry Sickness"

Patience is mysterious because it deals with the greatest physical mystery of our existence—Time. The sine qua non of stressed individuals is a panic about time. Nothing seems to be going fast enough, including themselves, and all of their actions are hurried, incomplete, and usually ineffective. This, of course, is due to the effect of noradrenalin on their heart, their blood pressure, and their brain. To the stressed individual, patience is torture, but it is a natural characteristic of the calm individual. Freed from the relentless pounding of noradrenalin, the calm individual is not terrified by the passage of time, does not need to conquer it, and does not feel opportunity slipping away at every moment. Instead he can experience that "today is the day the Lord has made, [and he can] rejoice and be glad in it[7]."

In our world, Time is a relentless stressor because it is an aspect of the physical Universe over which we have no control. We cannot compress it or expand it, bank it when we have a surplus, or withdraw it when we need it. We attempt to affect it by speeding <u>ourselves</u> up (something we are capable of doing) or slowing ourselves down (a definite challenge for most people). But we have no power over Time itself. Having no control over something is the formula for that item becoming a stressor in our lives.

In 1974 two cardiologists, Drs. Friedman and Rosenman, published their now famous popular book on *Type A Behavior and Your Heart.*[8] I am constantly amazed at the extent to which their labeling of the stressed individual as a "Type A" personality has penetrated popular culture. It is the rare person indeed who has not heard the phrase "Type A personality" to mean the very stressed individual.

---

[7] *The Holy Bible.* Psalm 118:24.
[8] Friedman, M. and Rosenman, R. *Type A Behavior and Your Heart.* Alfred A, Knopf. New York. 1974

Friedman and Rosenman made a fascinating observation. They noticed that the material on the furniture armrests in their waiting room was being worn down abnormally quickly, as was the carpet where patients rested their feet. They subsequently realized that this was due to the fidgeting of their patients' hands and feet while they were waiting to be seen. They ultimately discovered that the cause of this fidgetiness was that their patient population had high levels of circulating noradrenalin. This hyperadrenalism was the underlying condition that caused these patients to have hypertension and heart disease and led them to need the services of a cardiologist. Friedman and Rosenman called these patients Type A personalities. Friedman has continued to study Type A patients[9] and considers circulating noradrenalin levels to be an independent risk factor for heart disease[10].

Type A individuals have the following characteristics:
- explosive accentuations of key words in ordinary speech, even when there is no need for such accentuation
- a tendency to utter the final words of a sentence more rapidly than the opening words
- rapid eating, walking, speaking, moving.
- impatience with the rate at which most events take place
- impatience with waiting in line, performing repetitive tasks, reading, and cleaning up.
- a need to engage in multi-tasking—that is, always doing more than one thing at a time
- an incapability of listening to the topics others bring up
- feelings of guilt when relaxing

---

[9] Friedman, M. *Type A Behavior: Its Diagnosis and Treatment.* Plenum Pres. New York 1996.
[10] The others risk factors are 1) hypertension 2) family history of heart disease 3) high cholesterol 4) smoking and 5) diabetes.

- an inability to observe or enjoy details of the environments in which they may find themselves
- an inability to spare the time to develop the personal qualities worth <u>being</u> because of a focus on things worth <u>having</u>
- a tendency to schedule more and more in less and less time, resulting in a chronic sense of time urgency
- when meeting another type A person, a compulsion to challenge him or her
- the habit of banging one's fist on the table or into the other palm when speaking;
- a clenching of the jaw or frequent grinding of one's teeth, suggesting a continual internal struggle
- a belief that whatever success one has enjoyed has been due to being able to get things done faster than others
- evaluating everything in terms of numbers.[11]

Clearly the hallmark of a Type A person is a continual time urgency, or as Friedman and Rosenman call it—"hurry sickness".

Naturally if Type A patients are the patients at risk, there must be a comparison group—Type B individuals—whose sense of time is to be admired. Type B individuals are those people without high levels of circulating noradrenalin. Instead they have normal or even low levels. What are they like?

According to Friedman, unlike Type A's, Type B's do not suffer from "hurry sickness." They are able to eat without gobbling down the meal, they do not interrupt other people when listening, they do not have a free floating hostility which makes them compete at all times, they can play and relax without feeling a need to demonstrate

---

[11] Friedman and Rosenman. Op cit. 1974. pp 84-85.

their superiority, they can relax and have fun without guilt, and they can truly enjoy the company and interests of others. Basically, they are secure.

The conclusion from this analysis of time and the type A personality is this: Type A's never have enough time, because their inner sense of time is the experience of high circulating noradrenalin. Noradrenalin is the molecule of the acute stress reaction, and its message is "go faster." As a result, Type A people—acutely stressed people—cannot catch up with their need to go faster.

Because Type B personalities are not under the influence of noradrenalin, they can relax. For them, there is enough time. There is another day. As a result of the softening of time urgency, the body musculature relaxes, blood flow is redirected from the skeletal muscles to the body's core (internal organs), there is a change in the state of the nervous system from stress to relaxation, and the individual in whom this is happening passes from alarm to relaxation, pleasure and joy.

Breaking this sense of time urgency will, to your amazement, restore your sense of calm.

CHAPTER 9

THE EXPERIENCE OF CALM

Living Outside the Box

As the body begins to relax, it is natural for the irises of the eyes to relax as well, resulting in widened vision. With continued relaxation, the pulse slows, blood pressure normalizes, noradrenalin levels fall, and time urgency dissolves. There is now time to notice peripheral events and to bring them to conscious attention.

Early in my medical practice, I was an emergency room physician and became used to seeing acutely stressed individuals in tense situations. At first, I would race to a stretcher as it came through the doors, arriving breathless and incapable of taking in all the information the emergency responder was giving me. With experience, I learned to move more slowly, keeping myself unstressed. I found that in the relaxed state, it was easier to take in information, observe things out of the corner of my eye that might be relevant, and observe the situation as a whole. As my skills improved, I found that staying relaxed was contagious, often relaxing patient, family, and at times even the rest of the emergency room staff. By keeping the patient relaxed, I saved him from getting an unnecessary shot of noradrenalin from his own adrenal glands (the stress reaction).

In time, I came to see that there is also a deeper, meaning to "widen your vision". The mind, as well as the eyes, "visualizes". Many problems become unsolvable because the mind has narrowed its vision to the same thoughts over and over again, thoughts that have not produced a useful solution. Breaking the stress reaction, relaxing and "widening the mind" provides an opportunity for truly creative thinking—the now famous "out of the box" thinking.

I once read that whenever Carl Sagan, the now deceased popularizer of astronomy, conducted a meeting among his peers, he continually strove to enlarge the scope of the problems they were considering rather than narrowing them. I don't know that this is always a good strategy—eventually you have to make some decisions about pressing problems—but when patients are stuck on a problem for a long time, I do whatever I can to get them to widen their vision. I ask them to come up with a wide range of solutions for their problem or to tell me which previous problems in their life might have a similar solution. I ask them to make up new problems that might have a common solution with their current problem or to relate to me how other people in their family dealt with any problem.

Usually you find that the immediate problem the patient comes to you with is just one example of a much, much larger problem. For example, if they are having a specific relationship problem with a co-worker or boss, they may in fact be having massive relationship problems with everyone they know, because their fundamental problem is far bigger than they realize or want to discuss. But the bigger problem may be easier to solve than the little problem and, once solved, will have a far bigger impact on their life.

As a medical practitioner, you often have to be pretty relaxed about how long it is going to take you to solve some problems and be willing to have enough patience to discover the root cause of the difficulty.

"The box" is the mind in the grip of the stress reaction. If you really want to think "out of the box", break the stress reaction, have faith that you can solve the problem, pray for assistance, relax, take your time, and widen your vision. The solution is almost always outside the boundary you have drawn around the problem.

One of the boundaries that can exist around a problem is always seeing it from your point of view. Stressed people, of course, have to do everything by themselves. Relaxed individuals can benefit from the perspectives of other people.

Multiplying Viewpoints

Some years ago, when I first became interested in stress and its opposites, I became enamored of Zen meditation. This is, of course, far from unusual, because many people who seek to calm themselves do so through one of two primary routes: 1) diet and exercise and 2) religious faith and/or meditation. Because I enjoyed intellectual puzzles, I was fascinated by Zen Buddhism with its mind stopping questions called koans[1].

There is a wonderful Zen exercise called kinhin or walking meditation. Since I found it very difficult to sit still at first, walking meditation was (and still is) more pleasant for me. Of course, as my mind became calmer, sitting became easier. But by nature, I am a walker. One of the greatest benefits in my life from Zen practice came as a result of repeated kinhin—the benefit of perspective. Remembering perspective is a gift that never seems to stop giving.

To enjoy kinhin, imagine a large Japanese garden courtyard. Japanese gardens have beautifully groomed sand and interestingly placed rocks. Walking around them is a visual adventure, because they look different from each and every angle. Imagine that there is a path around this garden that is long enough to permit a slow, meditative walk. Perhaps it takes five or ten minutes to walk around it step by step, slowly enough to observe, to be aware of the surroundings.

---

[1] The most famous of these is, of course, "What is the sound of one hand clapping?" The most commonly assigned koan to beginners is "What is nothing?"

Usually in kinhin, the hands are held against the chest, in the hollow of the sternum, in-between the pectoral muscles and above the diaphragm. For convenience, and for a sense of stability, one method is to hold the left fist above the right, the thumb of the right hand being held upward, grasped inside the left fist. Or the hands may be held palms together at the same height as in meditative prayer. Usually one breathes in and out slowly as one walks, some relationship existing between the breathing and the walking, but the two are not bound together by any rule that would interfere with relaxed concentration.

As the walking progresses, your mind begins to slowly settle down, in the same way that a jogger's mind begins to settle after a certain stretch of jogging. Thoughts slowly progress from awareness of the thoughts inside your mind to perhaps the awareness of your body. After a further length of time, there is a further shift in awareness from one's mind or one's body to the features of the environment, a shift of awareness from one's inside to one's outside.

Whenever I did kinhin and reached the stage where I was no longer primarily aware of my inner thoughts but could now focus on outer reality, I was able to notice that the garden looked different with each step that I took. Of course, this was due to the fact that I was now at a different position in the garden. The tree that was originally in front of me was now at my left side, while the rocks that were originally blocked from my view by the tree were now plainly in sight. If someone had asked me to describe what I was seeing, I would have had to describe it differently at each step.

With the garden, the change in what one sees as one's perspective changes is obvious; yet, it is also subtle—so subtle, in fact, that it almost escapes notice. Now imagine that instead of observing a garden from different points of view, one is instead discussing a business decision, a political opinion, a marriage disagreement, or a point of privilege with one's teenager. The difference in each person's perspective, though equally obvious, also escapes notice.

Almost everyone knows the story of the blind men and the elephant; many people know such works of art as the movie *Rashomon*[2] or the cathedral paintings of Monet[3], both of which communicate the concept of point of view. Nevertheless, in tense and difficult situations, the idea that we are talking to a person who has a point of view different from ours seems to continually escape our notice. It becomes unconscious.

Once we become stressed, we see the world as us versus them. We attempt to validate our own point of view as the correct one and to invalidate everyone else's points of view as the incorrect ones. When we are calm, we see the world as us <u>and</u> them. We enjoy the world as seen by others and use it as the basis of communication and friendship.

Put most simply, no one else truly experiences the world the way you do or the way that I do. That simple fact throws each of us into a slight state of permanent loneliness because of our uniqueness. Almost all of us have a deep longing to share our perspective with another, to have someone else truly understand how we see the world. If we succeed in finding someone with whom this level of communication is achieved even for a short while, most of us experience a sudden surge of love, because complete communication <u>is</u> love.

Complete communication is so pleasant that without realizing it we can subtly begin to coerce our friends to agree with us just to experience this wonderful feeling of agreement again and again. But to get others to say that they really do see the world the way we do is an exercise in ego, not friendship. That strategy soon results in the replacement of friendship with power—the power of being right. Often the result is

---

[2] Kurosawa, Akira. *Rashomon*.

[3] Monet, Claude. I am referring to the paintings he made every hour of the Cathedral at Chartres, each of which shows the famous cathedral in a slightly different amount of light.

to force the person ever so slightly into submission, into the lie that they agree with us. The friendship then degenerates into an illusion.

A more lasting basis for a friendship is based on realizing that the other person must have a different viewpoint from ours if for no other reason than that they look at the universe from different coordinates in time and space.

Others are looking at a slightly different world from the one you're looking at. If you are calm, you can by-pass needing to dominate them with your point of view or defend against their dominating you with theirs. That realization leads to true joy.

Allowing Imperfections

Once one adopts the point of view that our individual lives are lived in a state of chronic stress, a lot of stories, like world history, Greek mythology, tribal fables, and family experiences fit nicely into place.

One of my favorites in this regard is the famous Navajo Rug Story. The way I originally heard it from friends in New Mexico is a little different from the way it is presented in books written by Navajos. So before giving it the slight twist that makes it fit more smoothly into my point of view, let me tell it the way I have read it in Navajo books.

The Navajo Indians live in the Southwestern part of the United States (Arizona, New Mexico). They are an ancient people with many skills, and one of the skills for which they are rightly admired is their skill in weaving distinctive, colorful rugs. These rugs occupy an important enough place in their culture to be accompanied by a myth that explains how they learned to weave them.

According to one story, their skill in weaving rugs comes from the gods. In fact, it was a gift to them from Spider woman, a Being from the Fourth World, who showed them how to produce the beautiful colors and designs[+]. She also instructed them that whenever they make a rug, they must weave into it a small opening—perhaps a different colored piece of yarn woven into the border at the edge of the blanket or some other imperfection—so that the weaver's spirit can escape from the center of the rug. Without the opening, the rug's perfection might trap the weaver's spirit.

In the version of the story as it was told to me, the reason for the imperfection relies on the observation that the world we live in is imperfect. A perfect rug, therefore, could never harmonize with the imperfect world. It would become a perfect creation in an imperfect world. The universe's need for consistency demands that this imperfection express itself at all times. If it cannot be in the rug, then perhaps it can find an outlet somewhere else, such as in the home of the rug maker—tearing or breaking something, or possibly causing an accident to a family member.

To prevent this from happening, the weaver allows the imperfection of the world to express itself in a deliberate mistake woven into the rug. Now the rug and the world can harmonize, and a free-floating imperfection looking for a place to land is averted.

From the time that I heard this second version of the rug story, it has had great value for me. It seemed to metaphorically capture some truth about our real existence. The immediate benefit was that I stopped worrying when my new car got its first scratch, or my new suit revealed its first stain. It's just the world's imperfection finding a place to express itself.

[+] Roessel, M. *A Navajo Girl Learns to Weave*. Lerner Publications Co. Minneapolis. 1995

Since then, the story has had an enlarging benefit in my life. Not everything can be perfect all the time, though we certainly can work towards perfection. No one can be perfectly beautiful, no work of art can achieve perfection, no social event can come off without a flaw, no person is always pleasant to be with. Increasingly, I can accept imperfection in myself and in others, and with it, an aspect of my stress level melts away. Someday, when God restores the Creation, all these imperfections will vanish; but, for now, they are unavoidable. Accepting them, rather than fighting them, reduces unavoidable stress.

A patient of mine who was very stressed agreed to construct a Holmes-Rahe scale for her life. We were working on her chronic stress list, eliminating some problems, adding others, when she made an important observation. "It never goes to zero, does it?" I agreed. Life that is nothing but accommodation becomes boring. People whose chronic stress score goes to zero either go nuts from the boredom or create problems to put a little spice in their life. For most people, however, this is not a problem. The next several stress problems are already in the mail.

Everything has a blemish or imperfection in it, even our lives. We cannot make anything perfect. To try to do so only creates a hardship somewhere else. We can make our work, our relationships, and our lives very beautiful like a Navajo rug; we can make our systems very safe, like our airplane transport system; but we cannot make them perfect. That task belongs to God alone.

Conscious Courage

Probably the most unexpected opposite of stress, which more than any other reveals that relaxation isn't all there is to non-stress, is courage. One of the prices we pay for confronting our stressors is the discovery that many of them are scary. In fact, it is because they are dangerous that we go into stress in the first place, dulling our consciousness, imagining that we might fight given half the chance, while often slipping into fear and escape.

Courage is best described by those who have experienced it; but because on the deepest levels we are all so similar, we also recognize courage when we observe it in others. We notice it in the stories of the signers of the Declaration of Independence; in the stories of the families, like the ten Boom's[5] in Holland, who hid Jews during the Second World War; in the words of newspaper publishers in repressive regimes; in the famous photo of the lone Chinese youth in Tianamen square, stopping a row of tanks by himself.

What makes courage such an opposite of stress is that it seems to be an act of the spirit, not of the mind and body. The courageous individual stays <u>conscious</u> in danger, and therefore does not succumb to fight or flight. What he and she communicate is that they can see the sick point in the center of the stressor, and they are irrevocably drawn to neutralize it as though they were the antidotes. Like the Zen arrow that becomes one with the bulls eye[6], the courageous individual is drawn by principle, seemingly beyond will, to locate and defy the sick point causing the stress, to say this far and no further. Thus Jesus becomes one with sin, absorbing it and destroying it in the process, and Buddha overcomes suffering by discovering its cause in the mind.

---

[5] Ten Boom, Corrie. *The Hiding Place.*
[6] Herrigel, E. *Zen and The Art of Archery.*

Many acts of true courage do not seem at all courageous to the person engaged in doing them. It is as though the event discovers the person; that by coming into existence, the event brings to public view a glimpse into the soul of a previously overlooked human being. It is as though the man or woman was born for that very moment. Jesus when speaking of the crucifixion said of Himself, "It was for this that I was born into this world."

Courage is an opposite of stress. Stressors can be frightening when confronted. Consciously following them to their source and negating them, rather than fleeing in fear, is clearly an act of courage. To the person watching, it may look extremely dangerous. To the person living it, it often has the quality of calm inevitability.

The Reward of Satisfaction

I will always be indebted to Mick Jagger for composing the lines, "I can't get no satisfaction." The song is, of course, a classic and so is the message.

At the time that he wrote it, Jagger was more successful in material terms than almost anyone listening to his music. He had access to the trappings of wealth and fame, and an excess of those things that matter the most to worldly young men. I realize that it is naive of me to assume that his song was the plaintive cry of a tortured soul who had tried all of earth's delights and come up empty. I assume it was more of an advertisement of just how much sensual pleasure he had already indulged in and how much more he was willing to experience. It would undoubtedly take a lot to satisfy him.

But still, I thought that there was a grain of truth in what he said, if for no other reason than that King Solomon had said the same thing in Ecclesiastes[7]. Solomon it will be remembered had said, "I have seen the works which have been done under the sun, and behold, all is vanity and striving after wind." (Ecc. 1:14)

The reason for this is obvious. Deep satisfaction is an experience which can never result from any experience in the physical world. It is true that one can be hungry and, by eating, satisfy the hunger; or be thirsty and, by drinking, satisfy that as well. But the way the word is used in this song, it means some deep, ultimate satisfaction, possibly sexual, but definitely psychological or spiritual in nature—something that lasts forever and improves with time. To last forever, things have to deepen or enlarge with time, because things that do not deepen with time ultimately fade. Examples are everywhere. It may have been satisfying to win a high school football game in which your school was a hopeless underdog, but the memory weakens ever so slightly with time and with repeated recall. I once hit a 2-out home run in the bottom of the ninth inning to win a camp baseball game, but that pleasant memory cannot remain at the same emotional pitch for the rest of my life that it had at the moment it occurred. Bobby Thompson's sensational 2-out ninth inning home run to win the National League pennant race in 1951 is certainly a more phenomenal, one-time ecstatic moment than mine was, but even it is not enough to truly satisfy the human soul. Even peak emotional or romantic moments fade with time, although the more spectacular they are at first, the longer they seem to last.

What satisfies the soul are not those items which appeal to the reptilian brain, the mammalian brain, or the human brain. What satisfies us are those items that appeal directly to the soul and spirit, because it is in this invisible realm—not in the body— where satisfaction is experienced.

---

[7] Ecclesiastes. *The Bible*.

If Jagger is telling the truth, he cannot get satisfaction because <u>satisfaction is not something you get</u>. <u>It's something you're left with after you give</u>. The song would be more poignant if he had said, "I can't <u>give</u> no satisfaction" because normally giving does lead to satisfaction. Make a child smile by touching his spirit, and you will have satisfaction. Heal a hurt, and you will have satisfaction. Relieve a human curse, as Drs. Horstman, Salk and Sabin did with polio vaccine, and you'll experience satisfaction. Free up people who are economic slaves to other people, as Dr. Muhammed Yunus[8] has done with his microcredit loans to the ultra-poor, and you will experience satisfaction.

Spiritual moments last forever because they are not experiences which exist in time. They continue to exist in the everlasting "Now" of the spiritual universe, and they <u>deepen</u> in significance, rather than fade, with the passage of time. Jesus taught this when he said "Do not lay up your treasures here on earth where moth and rust destroy, and where thieves break in and steal; but lay up for yourselves treasures in Heaven, where neither moth nor rust destroys and where thieves do not break in or steal." (Mt 6:19-20).

What does this have to do with stress? One reason people are stressed is that they "can't <u>get</u> no satisfaction". All the noradrenalin in the world will never produce satisfaction. It is not within the power of the stress reaction to wring satisfaction from the world, from another person, or from an achievement.

To get satisfaction, you need to break the stress reaction, go into non-stress, connect to the world, <u>give</u>, and then...voilà! "Satisfaction".

---

[8] Winner of Rotary International's 1999 Award for World Understanding—Rotary's highest honor.

Joy and More...

The goal of the stress free life is the experience of joy. The key that takes pleasure and relaxation and transforms it into joy is personal growth. Personal growth starts with identifying a problem and widening your vision to discover a solution. It continues with accepting your inadequacies for the job, activating your courage to move forward nevertheless, and then moving past your stress imposed boundaries more than you ever thought possible. To have real joy, you have to push the boundaries of your stress confined thinking into new territory.

Writing this book has been an experience of joy for me, because it has pushed me beyond what I have previously done and close to something—communication—which I value. Anyone who goes public with a creative work feels joy for the same reason, but as most successful artists and writers relate, if you stop at any level of achievement and simply repeat the previous experience, you will lose the joy. This is why successful people feel that they always have to push themselves beyond what they have already accomplished, to exceed their previous limits. They have to confront the stressful boundaries of their present circumstances and continue to grow. They have to widen their vision and pursue their dreams with courage.

Joy results from drawing closer to anything or anyone that you love. It can result from the inner experience of personal growth, from a deepening understanding of anything that interests you, from a new or deeper relationship with another person, or from a deeper experience with God.

...and much, much more.

It is the rare event indeed when the mindless, acute stress reaction is your best behavioral choice. Even in extreme physical danger, as martial artists have demonstrated time and again, the well trained, thinking mind adds a lot to your chances of survival.

There are lots of opposites of stress. Once you break the stress reaction, I am sure you will discover many for yourself. The secret is to connect to the situation, relax, be patient, widen your vision, and let the situation communicate with you. When your soul is touched, your Spirit will suddenly respond appropriately with the perfect next step. It will be guileless, ego less, appropriate to the situation, larger than the problem that called it forth, surprisingly relevant and effective, often courageous, and seemingly effortless. You will be genuinely humble, because you will experience that it seemed to come through you rather than from you. In the Far East, they gassho[9] in appreciation. In the West, you may end up thanking God for His intervention.

This can take many forms. It can be restoring your self-confidence after rejection, without being stressed that you are somehow not good enough. It can manifest as a willingness to be a friend and have friendships, even if other people are critical of whom you befriend. It can be learning to be a kid again, without the stress of thinking you're foolish; being curious about life without the fear that someone will ridicule your interests; reaching out to new groups of people; learning and developing new skills; recreating relationships with forgotten friends and family; pondering eternity; writing poetry; catching the soul and spirit of every situation; enjoying different cultures; paying attention to avenues of communication; practicing slowing down; spending time in Nature; contemplating the beauty of animals and plants; observing the nighttime sky; discovering something new; coming to peace with your financial life; and on and on, through connection rather than separation, awareness rather

---

[9] Gassho: Bow with palms touching.

than hiding, communication rather than isolation, interest rather than sophisticated boredom. There is, however, one common thread. You will always feel larger than you felt before. You will have grown, and growth produces joy.

*   *   *

The purpose of this book has been to describe the stress reaction so clearly from several points of view that its opposites can emerge from the shadows and be identified. When I was 4 years old, I saw New York City in an explosion of joy. It was the moment that World War II ended. The streets were filled with jubilant, happy people, hugging each other and jumping for joy. There was a feeling of euphoria in the air. To my small mind, it was as though everyone in the world had been invited to the best possible party.

On some level, I thought everybody in New York knew and liked each other, and since for me New York was all I knew of the world, at that moment you could have convinced me that the whole world was one large family that came together from time to time to party. I thought you could reach out to anyone safely, that everyone actually wanted to know who you were. I was stunned as I grew up to discover that isolation, not connection, is our reality.

That one incident revealed to me what is possible, if not here, then maybe in Heaven. We all sense that on some level we could connect. On that level there is calm—not stress.

PART IV

POST-TRAUMATIC STRESS DISORDER

OVERVIEW

POST-TRAUMATIC STRESS DISORDER

Most people do not suffer from post-traumatic stress disorder, which is why I placed this material at the end. It is not necessary to read it to benefit from the knowledge and advice in the first three sections of the book.

On the other hand, our current understanding of how the brain functions in post-traumatic stress disorder has led to a deeper understanding of the stress reaction in general. Readers who enjoy learning how the brain works will most likely find the material on post-traumatic stress quite fascinating and will have a strong foundation to understand new knowledge about the brain, as it is discovered in the future. This section is more technical than the book.

Chapter 10

The Special Case of Post-Traumatic Stress Disorder

Post-traumatic stress disorder (PTSD) is interesting, because the strategies that work for acute and chronic stress do not always work for PTSD. If you mistake PTSD reactions for normal chronic stress reactions, you may become frustrated by your inability to calm them. Yet they can be dealt with successfully.

Post-traumatic stress disorders are not simply reactions to circumstances that put you outside your comfort zone. They are conditioned fear reflexes to overwhelmingly frightening or life threatening events that occurred earlier in your life. This means that if you experience post-traumatic stress, the source of the stress is not in your immediate environment. It is in your memory, and it is being triggered by something in the present that is accidentally triggering the remembered traumatic event.

As I was beginning to write this appendix, there was a report on the nightly news that a Canadian military officer had developed a nervous breakdown after he had had the misfortune of observing a gruesome war scene, while serving as a U.N. peacekeeper. Apparently this officer was assigned to an African country, where a brutal civil war had been ongoing for many years. As an U.N. observer, he was specifically forbidden to intervene in the battles of this other country's civil war.

On the occasion that precipitated his breakdown, he was forced by orders to stand by helplessly while one side brutally killed and hacked to death men, women, and children of the other side. The combination of the horror of the war and his inability to influence the outcome—because of strict orders not to intervene—converged in him to produce a deep mental and spiritual disconnection. He became incapacitated by feelings of helplessness and experienced continuing flashbacks to the moments of horror.

Similar stories have, of course, been reported in American servicemen returning from Viet Nam, in rape victims, in people who suddenly lost parents or children to violence, and in individuals who survived enemy invasions of their towns or cities.

The definition of PTSD in medical texts is that it occurs after 1) an event that threatens or inflicts serious injury to oneself or others and that 2) it is a response characterized by intense fear, helplessness, or horror.[1] What makes it so unusual is that long after the event, afflicted individuals continue to experience flashbacks to the original trauma accompanied by the full-blown stress reaction that accompanied the initial experience. PTSD can result in psychological incapacitation, social withdrawal, and the avoidance of friends and family.

As recent research has begun to clarify this condition, there is a growing consensus that PTSD is a conditioned reaction to fear that by-passes the thinking mind and inputs directly into the limbic/emotional and reptilian/stress systems. Since the cause of the stress by-passes the conscious brain, the victim of post-traumatic stress does not realize what has triggered this intense stress reaction and may feel that he is losing his mind. He or she simply experiences intense emotional stress without knowing why it came about and has no idea how to stop it.

Joseph LeDoux, Ph.D. has done much of the new research on which the current view is based, and he has described his findings for the general public in his book *The Emotional Brain*.[2] There is also a large volume of scientific literature and historical experience about PTSD going as far back as World War II and described in a remarkable book about brain washing called *The Battle for the Mind*.[3]

---

[1] DSM-IV diagnostic criteria for PTSD (American Psychiatric Association, 1994).
[2] LeDoux, Joseph. *The Emotional Brain*. A Touchstone Book. Simon and Schuster, New York. 1998.
[3] Sargant, William. *The Battle for the Mind*: A Physiology of Conversion and Brain Washing. W, Heinemann Ltd. 1957. Republished Major Books, 1997.

Since understanding PTSD is based on fairly recent discoveries, much of the information presented here may undergo significant modifications in the future as newer discoveries are made. Nevertheless, I think you will see that enough is already understood to make this information useful right now.

Since the explanation relies on classical conditioning experiments, I need to review briefly the famous psychological experiments of Ivan Pavlov.

Pavlovian conditioning

As many people know, Ivan Pavlov was a Russian scientist who demonstrated that dogs could be conditioned to respond to unusual stimuli with predictable responses. In Pavlov's original experiment, an artificial stimulus (originally a bell) was paired with a specific event—the presentation of food to an animal. After many pairings of the bell with the food, the dogs begin to salivate at the sound of the bell, knowing that the food was coming. The crucial fact to retain about these experiments is that this conditioning occurs below the level of thought and consciousness. It is a reflex, akin to the knee jerk reflex.

In classical Pavlovian conditioning, it takes **many** pairings of the stimulus with the response to produce a subconscious association.

However, it is now known that if the stimulus is startling enough (for example, loud enough or frightening enough), the conditioning can take place even with a single exposure to the stimulus. This is called "one-shot conditioning", and it means that a single pairing of a stimulus with a response can create a conditioned reflex, if it is vivid enough.

__Example 1:__ A simple example of one-shot conditioning comes from the world of food. Many people have had the experience that on one occasion, when one of their favorite foods was prepared, something went terribly wrong with the ingredients and the final dish developed an unpleasant, perhaps even disgusting, smell or taste. The experience may have been so unpleasant that they were never able to eat that particular food again. Even an accidental remembrance of the incident can reactivate the unpleasant feeling. This overwhelmingly negative memory is an example of "one-shot conditioning."

Operant conditioning

Some years after Pavlov, B.F. Skinner discovered that animals could be conditioned to naturally occurring stimuli, if the reward or punishment immediately followed the action they were encouraged to perform. For example, if a rat accidentally touched a bar in his cage and he was rewarded with a pellet of food, it increased the chances that he would push the bar again. Conversely, if the rat were punished with an electrical shock each time he touched the bar, it reduced the chances that he would touch it again.

The only difference between this conditioning, which is called **operant** conditioning and classical Pavlovian conditioning, is that in classical conditioning the stimulus (the bell) is under the experimenter's control, whereas in operant conditioning, the stimulus is under the subject's control.

The way this applies to humans is that if you receive an injury from touching fire, you learn to be more cautious about touching it again. If you have fun the first time you ski, you are more likely to choose to do it again.

Fear conditioning

From the point of view of understanding post-traumatic stress disorder, the most important conditioning is <u>conditioning to fear</u>, because stress is most often a response to fear. Unlike classical conditioning and operant conditioning in which an <u>artificial</u> stimulus is paired to a response, God and Nature seem to have hard-wired into us (and other animals) fear conditioning to natural enemies. Thus, according to LeDoux[4] "rats will freeze and exhibit blood pressure and heart rate changes" typical of acute stress in the presence of a cat. "Because rats do not require prior exposure to cats to exhibit these responses, the cat is a natural trigger of defense responses for rats. ... Similar patterns of defense responses occur in humans and other animals when exposed to fear triggers (natural and learned)."[5]

Apparently we are born afraid of certain stimuli. The fear of falling seems to be universal in humans and may be hard-wired into our brains. Other fears can be learned very easily, by watching our parents or other role models act frightened in specific circumstances. We can learn fear quickly any time we encounter something dangerous and have a bad outcome. For example, an early experience of being bitten while reaching to pet a dog can produce fear, which is repeated each time any dog is encountered. Similarly, if an early experience of getting injections at the doctor's office is traumatic, the individual can carry this fear into future similar encounters. Sometimes these fears are learned without involvement of the conscious mind. **Thus it becomes possible to feel frightened without knowing precisely the original source of the fear.** Here is an extremely simplified version of how it happens.

---

[4] LeDoux, J. *The Emotional Brain.* Simon and Schuster, New York. 1998. pg. 144.
[5] Ibid.

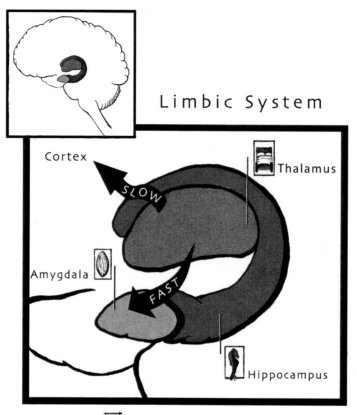

Limbic System

Cortex

SLOW

Thalamus

Amygdala

FAST

Hippocampus

The thalamus is the unconscious receiving area for all incoming sensory data (sight, sound, touch etc.). It has a *fast* path to the amygdala and a *slow* path to the cortex. If the cortex is conscious, it will send interpretive data to the amygdala and the hippocampus which will inhibit the stress reaction. If the cortex is 'unconscious', the amygdala will activate the stress reaction.

Figure 16

1) All sensory information coming in from the world, after it has first been gathered by the sense organs is fed into a structure in the midbrain called the **thalamus** (see Figure 16). Thalamus comes from the Greek word for bed or bedroom, so you can think of the sensory information coming in through our 5 senses as entering this large bedroom.

As far as we know, humans do not consciously experience sensations at the thalamic level, (although there is some suggestion that in cases of chronic pain, the pain may be arising at the thalamic level). The thalamus is an intermediate zone between the body's sensory receptors—like the eye and ear—and the interpretation of what those stimuli mean, which is a function of the cerebral cortex. In other words, the thalamus is like the post office where mail is collected from the community, processed, and then sent to different locations.

The thalamus sends its information to two different destinations: a conscious destination—**the cerebral cortex**—and an unconscious or reflex destination—the **amygdala** (see Figure 9) which is connected to the stress/relax system in the reptilian brain.

The unconscious destination, the **amygdala** (see Figure 16), leads to unconscious reflex behavior including the stress reaction. The conscious destination, **the cerebral cortex**, leads to a conscious appreciation of the events unfolding in the world and is capable of modifying the stress reaction.

When information arrives at the thalamus, it is sent to the amygdala for emergency evaluation and simultaneously to the cerebral cortex for conscious evaluation. Interestingly, the thalamus' messages to the amygdala arrive slightly ahead of those same messages to the cerebral cortex. Presumably this has survival value. For example, if I am afraid of bees, I don't want to be surprised by them. Therefore my brain needs to frighten me whenever any unknown flying object is in the air—even before I know whether or not it's a bee. Better to calm myself down later than mistakenly get bitten. The fast thalamus to amygdala pathway carries out this warning. Or, if you hear a sudden loud noise, you might want to reflexly react before you know for sure what the noise represents.

The amygdala relays this information to the stress system and you get a jolt of noradrenalin. The same information is simultaneously sent to the cerebral cortex where the incoming stimuli are decoded into their meanings. Perhaps it is just something falling off a shelf. If it turns out there is no danger, the cerebral cortex will override the amygdala, preventing the stress reaction.

The cerebral cortex sends continual messages back to the amygdala for more precise behavioral control. Now that I see the flying object is not a bee, but a bumblebee, which I know is not a threat to me, I can relax. Throughout the day, the cerebral cortex sends continually updated information to the amygdala so that the amygdala knows whether or not to maintain the fight/flight reaction or to turn it off.

2) **The amygdala** is thus the unconscious switch that decides whether or not novel stimuli should activate the fight/flight/freeze reaction. If the situation is frightening, "the amygdala...will cause your muscles to tense up, your blood pressure and heart rate to change, and hormones to be released, among other bodily and brain functions."[6] Conversely, if you can slow things down a bit by taking a deep breath, the cerebral cortex will then have time to update the amygdala with its more precise data as to whether or not the novel stimulus really requires stress system activation.

3) There is one more wrinkle that makes the stress activation system really interesting and explains PTSD. The cerebral cortex, having received information from the

---

[6] Ibid. p. 202.

160

thalamus for interpretation, not only sends its information to the amygdala to assist with decision making about the stress reaction, but it also sends the same information to a third structure called the **hippocampus** (see Figure 16), which puts the new information into a context of previous experience and learning. Yes, the flying object is a bee, but now that I look at it more closely, I can see that it is a bumblebee. I know from what I have read about bees that bumblebees don't sting, so I don't need to be afraid, and I can tell the amygdala to turn off the stress reaction. Noticing that it is a bumblebee is a function of the cortex—the thinking brain. Knowing that bumblebees don't sting is an association brought to consciousness by the actions of the hippocampus, part of the associative brain.

The **hippocampus** is sometimes called "the brain within the brain" and is analogous to the card catalog in a library. If you look something up in the library catalog, it will tell you everything that is related or connected to it. If I say to you, "John Kennedy" everything that you can associate with that name—the Presidency, his appearance, Jackie, Cuba, the assassination, your feelings about him—will all come to mind. The hippocampus activates these associations. It associates everything you can think of to a given stimulus or to a given event. "Through the hippocampal system you will remember who you were with and what you were doing during [a traumatic event] and will also remember, as a cold fact,[7] that the situation was awful."

Bear in mind: The current view is that the hippocampus associates any event with all the knowledge and emotions that you have ever associated to that event.

---

[7] Ledoux, Joseph. *The Emotional Brain.* p.202

How to use this information

The research on the hippocampus and amygdala just described suggests that there is a "quick and dirty" response (LeDoux) to stimuli that put you out of your comfort zone. This response is the unconscious thalamus ---> amygdala ---> fight/flight/freeze reaction—what we have come to know as the acute stress reaction. There is also a slower thalamus -> amygdala -> cerebral cortex -> hippocampus system, which says "Wait a minute. No reason to get bent out of shape. This is something we already know how to handle."

The importance of this information is that it underscores the point that if you can just break the unconscious stress reaction, updated information from the cerebral cortex will arrive a split second later, the hippocampus will widen your vision to include a vast array of knowledge and associations, and you'll make a better decision. If you panic, you will make an unconscious decision. If you breathe and break the stress reaction, you will make a conscious decision, <u>augmented by a lot of associative information retrieved by the hippocampus</u>.

"Consider another example. You are walking down the street and notice someone running towards you. The person, upon reaching you, hits you on the head and steals your wallet or purse. The next time someone is running towards you, the chances are a set of standard fear responses will be set into play. You will probably freeze and prepare to defend yourself, your blood pressure and heart rate will rise, your palms and feet will sweat, stress hormones will begin to flow through your bloodstream, and so on. The sight of someone running toward you has become a conditioned fear stimulus. But suppose you later find yourself on the street where you were mugged. Although there is no one running toward you, your body may still be going through its defense motions. The reason for this is that not only did you get conditioned to the immediate stimulus directly associated with the trauma (the sight

162

of the mugger running toward you), <u>but also to the other stimuli that just happen to</u> <u>have been there. These made up the occasion or context in which the mugging took</u> <u>place, and like the sight of the mugger they too were conditioned by the traumatic</u> <u>experience.</u>"[8] (Emphasis mine).

Post-traumatic stress disorder

What happens in post-traumatic stress disorder is that an individual finds himself in a frightening situation of great intensity. The fear is great enough that the person <u>becomes conditioned below the level of consciousness</u> to the perceived stimuli. This happens in a reflex manner, identical to Pavlovian or Skinnerian style conditioning. It is a "one-shot conditioning."

From that moment on, whenever any stimuli similar to those of the original event are perceived, the individual will re-experience maximum stress, just as Pavlov's animals salivated every time they heard the bell. It's simply a conditioned reflex, and it cannot be extinguished by simply talking to the person. The result is post-traumatic stress disorder, a condition in which an individual becomes easily startled or frightened for no apparent reason and has undesired flashbacks to a moment of trauma without warning. As can now be appreciated, it is the conditioned reflex nature of the disorder that accounts for its symptoms.

Treatment of PTSD

There is no general agreement in the psychiatric or psychological literature on which treatments work and which do not in treating post-traumatic stress disorder.

---

[8] Ibid. pgs. 165-167.

Part of the problem in scientifically investigating the results of treatment is that so many people in distressing circumstances seem to recover on their own without any intervention. In fact, "Toxic events occur in very high frequencies even in civilian life in peacetime, yet this high prevalence is not matched by high prevalence rates for event-attributed distress disorders such as Acute Stress Disorder and PTSD."[9]

Apparently when it is studied, the most important factors in determining whether PTSD will develop in a particular person are <u>not</u> the enormities of the event itself, but rather the long-standing qualities that the individual possessed prior to the event, especially their underlying belief systems. "Most people show short-lived distress that is not clinically significant, then recover, showing resilience and adaptation. A small percentage show event-attributed distress syndromes of clinical magnitude, a different small proportion show highly idiosyncratic responses including exhilaration or gains in confidence, and some show event-attributed distress syndromes in the absence of any significant exposure. These individual differences mean that post-event symptom reports need to be understood more in the context of long-standing features of temperament and individual beliefs than is provided for in the event-oriented model."[10]

In other words, some people become stronger following even the most extreme circumstances, some collapse in the face of minor overwhelm, and most people simply recover from even the most overwhelming traumas.

So what are the most important factors in getting over PTSD? In my own experience, the most crucial factor is the person's worldview prior to being in the circumstance. Although there may be no scientific studies that absolutely pin this down, general world experience is that people who have survived—even grown—under the

---

[9] Bowman, M. *Individual Differences In Post-Traumatic Response. Problems with Adversity-Distress Connection.* Lawrence Erlbaum Associates, Publisher. London. 1997. pg. 135.
[10] Ibid. pg. 136.

most adverse circumstances are people like Terry Anderson, Nelson Mandela, Joni Eareckson Tada, John McCain, and Corrie ten Boom, people who either had strong fundamental beliefs about life and death or else, like Viktor Frankl, developed them during the events themselves. Using the model I described above for the way the body handles fear, this can perhaps be explained.

An individual's world view—beliefs about life and death, beliefs about why things happen the way they do, about whether or not God can be relied upon for supernatural help in the worst of circumstances—all of these seem to be associated in the hippocampus as though there were a card in the "Hippocampal Catalogue" entitled "My Deepest Beliefs about Everything".

Since the fear response generated by the amygdala is <u>conditioned</u> by input from the hippocampus, the crucial question is "What's in the hippocampus on this topic?"
If the hippocampal worldview is big enough and wide enough to keep a person conscious and sane during the stress of terror-filled events, the amygdala will be coaxed into reducing its activation of stress. As a result, the body will not suffer the ravages of non-stop noradrenalin and cortisol.[11]

Conclusion: The best defense against PTSD is a worldview that is wide enough to encompass anything that can happen.

---

[11] In the chapter on chronic stress, I left out an interesting fact about chronic stress and the hippocampus, because I hadn't yet mentioned the role of the hippocampus in stress. But interestingly enough, under the prolonged cortisol stimulation of chronic stress, the hippocampus itself shrinks in size. Presumably this means that is harder to make rich associations, when chronically stressed.

Psychiatrists, Psychologists, Clients and Spirituality

Much the same point is made in a recent book on PTSD called *Facilitating Posttraumatic Growth* by Calhoun and Tedeschi[12]. These authors ask the question, "What should therapists know about spirituality or religion?" and they answer "a lot."[13] They point out that the clinician needs to know a lot about the client's spirituality and a lot about their own. What I discovered in my own practice was that people who suffered PTSD often lacked a clearly enunciated faith in anything prior to the trauma—or something worse, a faulty strut supporting their faith. As a result, when the principle they had faith in didn't materialize, they lost all their faith.

Calhoun and Tedeschi point out that "It may also be useful if the clinician can develop an early understanding of the degree to which spiritual beliefs have been shaken, shattered, or already modified in the wake of trauma. Although spiritual assumptions appear to be more [resilient] than empirical assumptions about the world [beliefs based upon one's own observations], many persons experience some degree of challenge to important philosophical assumptions. Having a good sense of what the individual's spiritual beliefs were before, what they are now, and which important assumptions are still being ruminated about can be helpful in attending to the spiritual issues that emerge in counseling."[14] In other words, your best defense against traumatic stress disorder is a religious, spiritual, scientific, or philosophical world view that can incorporate any level of mindless violence or trauma and still make sense out of life.

---

[12] Calhoun, L.C. and Tedeschi, R.G. *Facilitating Post-traumatic Growth. A Clinician's Guide.* Lawrence Erlbaum Associates, Publishers. London.. 1999
[13] Ibid. page 116.
[14] Ibid. pg. 117.

The Incredible Role of Doubt

As a result of working with PTSD patients, I began to realize that our beliefs about the world are crucial to our mental health and to our resistance to stress. From working with people's worldviews, I noticed that people who get the most inner strength from their worldviews are people <u>who can experience doubt about their views and not crumble</u>. They enjoy the strength it gives them to ponder the foundations of their faith, because each pondering gives them renewed energy in what they believe. People who shun debate and cannot tolerate any doubt about their faith whatsoever make me think that it would not take much to collapse their entire belief structure.

Having been trained in science, I am very familiar with the important role that doubt plays in understanding scientific concepts. Far from being subversive, doubt leads to inquiry, which leads to discovering the truth abut something, which leads to greater faith. In other words, great doubt leads to great faith[15]. Here is how it works:

Imagine that your deepest belief systems are stored throughout the brain, but access to them is stored in a single area, where all the associations to your belief system can be brought together to form a worldview. Think of this belief system as if it were a table with many legs[16]. The table is the belief system, and the legs are the facts or evidences on which the belief system rests. If someone can kick out or destroy one of the legs of the table, your belief system will now rest on a slightly shakier foundation. If they can kick out two or three legs from under the table, your belief system may start to wobble. A few more legs and it will come crashing down. At this point you don't know what to believe.

---

[15] This is a concept which I first encountered in a book by Kapleau, Philip. *The Three Pillars of Zen*. Anchor Books . 1980. p.64-65.

[16] I first heard this metaphor on an Anthony Robbins tape. I don't know whether he invented it or heard it from someone else.

If you are being brainwashed or coming under the influence of a cult, the person (or persons) who have been systematically destroying your belief system will now supply you with the new legs (beliefs) on which your new belief system (table) will rest. You have now been converted to a new worldview.

I have presented this change of belief systems as if it were a bad thing. But it can also be a very good thing. In fact, it is the usual operating mode of science. Scientists in any field have a worldview on which they base their theories and their new discoveries. Occasionally a new discovery, like the orbiting of the earth around the sun, will become apparent and contradict the previous worldview (that the sun moved around the earth). The new discovery will start to kick out the foundations of the previous scientific theory. At first there will be a battle between the two opposing views, because there may be a lot of observational evidences on which the old theory was based. But as more and more observations are made, sooner or later one of the worldviews will prevail. This has been detailed wonderfully by Thomas Kuhn in his very famous book, *The Structure of Scientific Revolutions.*[17]

With that discussion as foundation, we can now see the magnificent role that doubt plays in both scientific revolution and in strengthening a person's world view. No matter how elegantly we construct our worldview, there are going to be weak points. This is true whether it is based on philosophy, science, the Bible, Buddha's teachings, or any other holy work or scripture. This is because our understanding of any worldview is incomplete. As a result, we walk around with a lot of untested struts holding up our belief systems.

From time to time, life throws us a curve. It can come through experience, through reading, or just through day dreaming and thinking. All of a sudden we realize that something we hold dear—a cherished thought or belief—might not be true. A little

---

[17] Kuhn, Thomas. *The Structure of Scientific Revolutions.* University of Chicago Press 1996.

doubt creeps into our thinking. Although it makes us uncomfortable, this is actually about the best thing that can happen to us. If we have the strength and the will power to notice it, we can track down the weak strut in our belief system, one that may have been put into place during a non-reflective moment. Perhaps an incorrect piece of data is stored there or a concept that is misunderstood. If we can locate it, find out what the true data or piece of information should be, correct it and replace the strut, it will be stronger than ever. Our faith will actually increase.

On the other hand, people who are not used to working with doubt often consider it to be a sign of weakness, or lack of faith, to doubt what they are learning when they study their faith. This is what leads to cults—people who refuse to question or doubt their leader.

Doubt makes us stronger, because when a crunch moment of life trauma comes, our belief systems will be more resilient if the weak spots to which the doubt was pointing have been analyzed and repaired. This is especially valuable while in school. Because students have so much homework to do each night, there is little opportunity for them to realize that some information they are being taught rests on shaky foundations. Yet they are recording it, memorizing it, and regurgitating it as though no one had any doubts about its validity. Paying attention to doubt is one of the hallmarks of intelligence and of effective learning. It strengthens your worldview, and it protects you from being shaken by life's traumas.

So what <u>can</u> be done for people who, nevertheless, develop PTSD?

Treating PTSD has to be a two-pronged attack:
  i) On the one hand, the therapist or therapeutic group has to stop the incessant activation of the stress reaction by all of the triggers that are stimulating it. These triggers include the ones that are directly related to the event and

the ones that have accidentally become conditioned into the event.

ii) The second step is to determine whether the individual with PTSD has a shattered view of self as a result of the trauma and slowly assist him or her in building back an acceptable world view.

Stopping the incessant activation of the acute stress reaction:

A variety of techniques have been devised to break the incessant stress reactions that the terrifying, post-traumatic stress disorder memories activate. For most techniques this part of the process has two elements: 1) some manner in which the terrifying memory is <u>safely</u> relived so that it can be affected by treatment, and 2) some manner in which the terrifying memory no longer activates the stress reaction.

I'll give you a few examples of techniques so that the general method becomes apparent. Which technique should be used for any given patient's problem has more to do with what the therapist treating the patient has been trained to do than with the demonstrated superiority of any one method over another.

<u>Neurolinguistic programming</u>: Developed by Richard Bandler and John Grinder[18] and popularized by Anthony Robbins[19], NLP can be rapid and dramatic. It is based on the idea that the brain has to go through certain steps to re-create the stress response each time it is activated by the terrifying memories. If one can interfere with these steps, the stress reaction will not be activated.

In one NLP technique, you are first directed to dissociate yourself from the event by watching it happen on a movie screen rather than remembering it as happening to

---

[18] Bandler, Richard, and Grinder, John. *Frogs Into Princes*. Real People Press. 1979.

[19] Robbins, Anthony. *Personal Power*. Tape Series. Robbins Research International, Inc. San Diego, CA. 1993.

you personally.[20] This satisfies the need to safely relive the experience. To dissociate from the feelings that the event provokes, you imagine yourself sitting in the balcony or projection booth of a movie theater, watching yourself sitting on the main floor of the movie theater, watching the movie of the event.[21] From this safe distance of being doubly removed from the memory, you are instructed to watch the traumatic event unfold sequentially on a movie screen to a point in time past the trauma, then jump mentally inside the screen and run the picture backwards. By running it backwards, you distort the <u>sequencing</u> that is crucial to the activation of the stress reaction. You now continue to run it forwards and backwards weakening the reflex associating the event to the stress reaction.

Next, you further distort the crucial features of the memory by changing the facial features of the people in the memory, by changing what they are wearing, doing, or saying, or adding people to the scene who come to assist you. You can change it in any way you wish so that the memory loses its connection to the stress reaction. The connection to the stress reaction is weakened each time the memory is replayed in an altered fashion. Attempts to run it correctly are permanently hampered by the new associations that become mentally glued to it. The result is a weakened post traumatic stress memory.

Eye Movement Desensitization and Reprocessing: A second technique, eye movement desensitization and reprocessing (EMDR) does something similar. It interferes with the traumatic memory by interfering with the eye muscle tensions that are associated with the memory. This is because part of the processing of any memory is information that tells the eye muscles where to move the eyeballs to "see" the memory. In EMDR the patient focuses his or her attention on the memory while

---

[20] As will be seen in the discussion which follows on hypnosis, dissociation is effective for treating PTSD, because people who develop PTSD very commonly are people who dissociated during the original event. (op cit. Spiegel and Cardena).

[21] Bandler, Richard. *Using Your Brain for a Change*. Real People Press. Moab, Utah. 1985. pg. 43-46.

simultaneously watching the therapists finger as it is moved back and forth. The idea, again, is to break the sequencing of the memory (because it involves instructions to the eyeballs on where to move) thus weakening the ability of the memory to activate the stress reaction.

Hypnosis: The success of hypnosis is very much dependent on the skill of the therapist and the extent to which the patient feels safe with the therapist. According to hypnotherapists Spiegel and Cardena[22], hypnosis is of value in the treatment of PTSD because individuals who develop PTSD are likely to have dissociated during the trauma of the original event. In fact, this dissociation may be the reason that the individual developed PTSD in the first place, since the event is now held in dissociated memory.

"Dissociated" means that the person who experienced the trauma had feelings of unreality, an altered sense of the passage of time, a sense of detachment, or a sense of no control. In other words, the individual who subsequently develops PTSD is often someone who went into a dissociated state during the fright of the event as a means of self-protection (mental flight). Treatment requires recreating the dissociated state and restoring control of the memories to the victim. Seen this way, PTSD is simply the acute stress reaction being triggered below the level of conscious awareness, again and again. The goal of at least one phase of therapy is to interfere with this reflex[23].

Virtual Reality Therapy for PTSD: The most exciting new development in the treatment of PTSD is Virtual Reality Therapy, a therapy pioneered as a collaborative

---

[22] Spiegel, D. and Cardena, E. New Uses of Hypnosis in the Treatment of Posttraumatic Stress Disorder, *J. Clin. Psychiatry*. 51:10 (suppl), October 1990.

[23] This is _not_ to be confused with memory retrieval, a now discredited technique in which people are told they can recover memories of abuse they have forgotten. PTSD patients can remember what happened to them—that is why they are so continually stressed. What they need to realize is that those events happened in the past and that now, in the present, they are safe.

effort at New York-Presbyterian Hospital/Weill Cornell Medical Center and the University of Washington's Interface Technology Laboratory in Seattle.[24] This technique assists patients in confronting their fears by seeing the situation that frightens them in virtual reality, rather than by re-imagining the real incident.[25] This technique shares with Neurolinguistic programming the ability to confront and deal with the source of fear from a safe distance.

Treating PTSD most often requires professional assistance. Without professional treatment, what most PTSD victims try to do for themselves is to isolate themselves from almost everyone and everything in the belief that a massively controlled environment will reduce the number of cues that activate the stress reaction. This is why Viet Nam veterans so often move deep into the woods or to an environment that feels very safe to them. It limits their exposure to novelty and therefore to the accidental triggering of stress. Their goal is that over time, the number of stimuli triggering the stress reaction will decrease and the horrible memory itself will fade. Unfortunately, fear conditioning once established has proved to be very long lasting, so that at this time therapy seems to be preferable to personal isolation.

Rebuilding a world-view

In working with post-traumatic stress patients myself, I noticed that I often had to answer their questions about how God could have allowed something like their traumatic experience to occur or how, on a fundamental level, the kind of evil that happened to them could even exist. In Paul Tillich's words, "the foundation of everything" had collapsed. Everything they previously had thought was true about

---

[24] For information see *http://www.hitl.washington.edu/projects/ptsd*

[25] A website for commercial virtual reality treatments for phobias can be found at *www.virtuallybetter. com*

the world, all their most deeply held beliefs, had been shattered. Their conceptual world had collapsed, and nothing they were aware of could take its place. If they had been raped or a victim of a war atrocity, they felt that they could never be safe again. Terror could appear at any moment. For many people, only group therapy with people who had experienced the same terror they had experienced could offer even temporary feelings of safety.

Treatment of PTSD can be lengthy and at times painful, but it can succeed. The stimuli causing the startle reaction can be located and flattened. The individual can learn to make discriminations between the rare, violent person or group that they encountered and the fact that most people and groups would not behave so savagely. The patient can learn that memories of the events will not cause harm in the present or make them more vulnerable in the future to similar events; they can learn that they will not lose control of their behavior if the memory should re-surface. They may want to learn self-defense. Often martial arts training will give them a sense of empowerment and make them feel less vulnerable. And they need to take spiritual inventory to discover if there is a religious or spiritual belief system in which they can once again place their faith.

Restoring Calm

It takes an immense amount of work to restore a sense of inner calm after developing PTSD, but it can be done. I know this because people exist who have done it, and reading their stories can be inspiring.

The steps are the ones I have just mentioned:
   i. The triggers for the recurring acute stress reaction have to be identified and inactivated. Usually this requires professional assistance.

ii. The sufferer from PTSD has to find a belief system large enough to explain how it could be that people engage in evil behavior; or if the source of the stress was a natural disaster, how it can be that such events occur.

iii. Usually, you need to begin a daily spiritual practice that connects you to God or Self, as you understand those terms.

iv. Slowly you begin to separate out the specifics of the traumatic event as being unusual and unlikely to be repeated, while normal life is seen as less frightening.

v. It can be very strengthening to take up some form of self-defense or martial arts.

… and finally, practice being alert and calm.

Index

A

accommodation 9
     and stress scale 75-77
     and chronic stress 93-99

ACTH 60

acute stress reaction 10-11
     overcoming 12-17
     biologic basis 21-23
     reptilian brain 25-26, 35-39
     emerging from 31
     distinct from chronic stress 55-62
     Type A 129-132
     PTSD 162, 170-174

adrenalin 39

allergic response 61

amygdala 45
     and PTSD 159-162, 165

anxiety 53, 100, 106, 123

appeasement 45

awareness 12, 21, 29, 36, 49, 136, 146, 172

B

boredom ii, 7, 57, 80, 88-92, 106, 117, 140, 147

C

cerebral cortex 12
     human brain 29-33, 46, 48
     boredom 89-91
     problem solving 101-108
     PTSD 159-162

choking 42

chronic stress load 78

chronic stress reaction 73

E

endurance 55, 59, 60

ethical boundaries 6

ethics 36, 112

experts 97, 101, 104, 111

Eye Movement Desensitization 171

F

faith ii
>   in chronic stress 67-71
>   and coping 94-103
>   in oneself 117
>   in God 119, 125-127
>   and problem solving 134
>   and PTSD 166-169, 174

fight 4
>   acute stress 11, 23, 25, 30, 31, 35, 36, 37, 39, 42, 43, 44, 48, 49
>   chronic stress 53, 56, 57, 58, 59, 90
>   coping 93, 102, 103, 104, 106
>   daredevils 115, 118
>   courage 141
>   PTSD 160, 162

flight ii
>   acute stress 4, 11, 23, 25, 30, 31, 36, 37, 39, 40-45, 48-49
>   chronic stress 53, 57-59, 68
>   coping 90, 93, 102-106
>   courage 141
>   and PTSD 160, 162, 172

flow 13, 107, 109

foundation of everything 127, 173

Frankl, Victor 69, 102

freeze 4
>   acute stress 36-37, 45, 48-49
>   endurance 58-59
>   PTSD 157, 160, 162

M

MacLean, P.D. 22

mammalian brain 23, 26, 27, 29, 45, 124, 143

N

nature 12, 69, 135, 143, 163

neurolinguistic programming 170, 173

O

optimism 37, 65

overwhelm 80, 95, 98, 164

P

pain 5, 7
    acute stress 9, 15, 48
    chronic stress 53, 56-57, 59, 90
    coping 100, 109, 112
    and connection 115-116
    faith 119
    prayer 128
    and PTSD 159

Pasteur 110, 111

patience 4, 15, 128-129, 134

Pavlov 155-156, 163

Peale, Norman Vincent 126

perception 15, 75, 118

persistence 97, 99, 101-102

perspectives 135-137

pessimism 65

pleasure
    pursuit of 3-7
    stress and 47-48
    problem solving 101
    learning 107

and daredevils 115-116
Type B 132
satisfaction 142
joy 145

post-traumatic stress 16, 119, 151-173

prayer
acute stress 13
chronic stress 58
will and spirit 69-70
coping 95, 99
faith 126-128

R

rage 30, 37, 57, 100

relaxation 31, 87

reptilian brain
and acute stress 23-26, 29-31, 35-36, 44-49, 124
and dare devils 115-116
satisfaction 143
PTSD 159

S

safety 5, 9, 58, 101, 174

satisfaction ii, 70, 142, 143, 144

Seligman, Martin 37, 65-66, 95

Skinner, B.F. 65, 156

Social Readjustment Scale 75

spirit 39, 58-59, 68-71, 110, 120, 139, 141-146

stress ii, iii
acute 4-19, 50
and triune brain 21-26
and human brain 29-33
and reptilian brain 37-39
chronic 53-92
and coping 93-100
and problem solving 102-120
opposites of 123-147